Belonging
WORKBOOK

FOR USE WITH THE BELONGING DVD SERIES

TWELVE WEEK COURSE WORKBOOK

Jim Wilder and Ed Khouri

Belonging is the second module in the
Thriving: Recover Your Life Series

Shepherd's House Inc.
P.O. Box 40096
Pasadena, CA 91114

www.lifemodel.org
www.thrivingrecovery.org

© 2010 by E. James Wilder, Ph.D. and Rev. Edward M. Khouri Jr.

Published by Shepherd's House Inc.
P.O. Box 40096
Pasadena, CA 91114
www.LifeModel.org

ISBN number 978-1-935629-02-3

Amplified Bible Scripture quotations are from: The Amplified Bible(R) Copyright ©1954, 1958, 1962,1964, 1965, 1987 by The Lockman Foundation, La Habra, CA 90631. All rights reserved.

RSV Scripture quotations are from: The Revised Standard Version. 1971, Logos Research Systems, Inc.: Oak Harbor, WA.

NKJV Scripture quotations are from: The New King James Version. 1996, 1982, Thomas Nelson: Nashville.

Parenting from the Inside Out as referenced in Chapter 3 is written by Daniel J. Siegel and Mary Hartzell, New York: Penguin Group, 2003.

For more information about the work of Dr. Suzanne Day as referenced in Chapter 3 and in the Shalom for my Body Long Form located in the Appendix, please visit: www.wisechoiceeducationalservices.com.

The Lehman Relational Connection Circuit Checklist as referenced in Chapter 3 is by Karl Lehman M.D., and is used by permission. For further information, visit www.kclehman.com.

 "Faith and Preparation" by Dr. Willaim Ames is referenced in Chapter 8 and can be found on the website "A Puritan's Mind," at: www.apuritansmind.com/William%20Ames/WilliamAmesFaithPreparation.htm.

*For further information about Thriving: Recover Your Life and other Thriving modules,
please visit: www.ThrivingRecovery.org*

TABLE OF CONTENTS

Acknowledgments & Appreciation

This workbook, Belonging and the entire Thriving: Recover Your Life project would not be possible without the joyful support, practical help and the friendship of many different people.

Maritza, as always you are a joy, and your smile is still the most beautiful thing I look forward to every morning. We practice our Belonging Skills together and there are so many things I've found to appreciate about you! Thank you for being so gracious to me and giving me the time I need to teach and write.

Christian and Rebecca, you learned and practiced these skills with us. I am still so encouraged by the next generation of recovery leaders who have actually learned and applied the skills they need to thrive personally, and in their marriage, work and ministry.

The staff at Shepherd's House: Maribeth Poole, Kitty Wilder, and David and Jan Takle volunteered to be the initial Belonging Coordinators at Paz Naz. Your feedback and help developing Belonging are greatly appreciated!

Alan and Steve, thank you for your incredibly valuable input and highly valued friendship. You help make Equipping Hearts work!

Thanks to the Thriving groups at New Life Christian Fellowship in North Carolina and Paz Naz in California, and all the Belonging Beta Groups, because you helped us develop, test and refine Belonging. Special thanks for the Hayward Group for their early work with Belonging.

Chris and Jen Coursey, thank you for your work with Thrive, your friendship, partnership and work with producing the Share Immanuel Booklet.

Karl and Charlotte Lehman are the original Immanuel Process pioneers, and Karl's ground breaking work with relational circuits and the Lehman Relational Connection Circuit Checklist helped make Belonging possible.

Thanks to Ian Galindo and John Messer for their work filming the Belonging Teaching Video, the Belonging Coordinator Video and portions of the Belonging Facilitator Training Video. Thanks for Tony Parker and Jordan Courtney for helping to complete the filming of the Belonging Facilitator Training Video. We would also like to thank Gary & Susan Bauer and Gavin McCune for their incredible editing that makes us all look better!

Special thanks to James Benfield at 24/7 Fitness in Hickory, North Carolina. Your work with me is part of my healing journey, and you are helping my body thrive!

Welcome to Belonging!

BELONGING IS THE JOY WE CREATE AROUND OURSELVES.

Welcome.

You and I are starting a new journey together. In Forming, we learned to sail in our relationship with God, and discovered the wonder of God's interactive voice and presence. In Restarting, we encountered the transforming power of joy as we learned to build increasing levels of joy in our relationships with God and with others. In both Forming and Restarting, we've discovered that we are created for relationships, and that only in joyful relationships with God and others are the deepest longings of our heart fulfilled.

In Belonging, this journey gets even better. Building on the practical relational skills that we have developed in Restarting and/or Forming, we are about to take relationships with God and others to a whole new level. In Belonging, you and I will discover how to create a joyful place all around ourselves that extends an open invitation to others to come and share our joy with us. Belonging is the joy we create around ourselves!

What will Belonging do for my relationships with God and other people?

Everything about Belonging is designed to help you grow deeper, life-giving relationships with God and with others!

Growing with God

If you have been through Forming, you've already spent 12 weeks learning and practicing exercises that have nurtured your relationship with God. We've found ourselves increasingly captivated by God's interactive presence, and listened as He's shared His heart with us. We've discovered that experiencing God's presence and learning to interact with Him are the keys to spiritual formation and transformation. While "working really hard to be good and doing all the right things" may sound good, they are ultimately spiritually, emotionally, mentally and physically exhausting – and do not lead to the kind of heart transformation that God – and we – desire. But, as we have practiced our exercises and learned to simply "be with God," talk with Him, share our hearts with Him and hear His heart, we've found the joy, peace and love that we want the most.

If you've completed Restarting, you have also discovered the joy of listening to God and experiencing His presence. As our capacity for joy and peace has increased, so has our ability to perceive God's presence, hear His voice and know His heart. As we've practiced the Immanuel Process, we've improved our ability to connect directly with God and experience His heart for us in both places of joy and in painful places of life. Our Scripture meditation exercise helped us learn to talk with God about scripture, listen to Him and journal our experiences. Discovering God's heart and presence has begun to transform us!

In Belonging, all of us will continue growing our relationships with God. Weekly Bible stories will help us connect more deeply with Him, and help us better recognize and understand His heart for relationship. We'll learn how simple things like learning to live in appreciation and shalom (God's Peace) engage the relational centers of our brain so that we can form a stronger, deeper and more interactive connection with God. Learning to receive validation and comfort from God will calm and quiet us if we're upset – and help develop the incredible gift of Godsight, which allows us to see ourselves, other people and our situations from God's perspective. Most importantly, we'll learn new exercises and skills that will help an ongoing, interactive connection with God become more of our "normal" emotional and relational experience. Would you like to learn how to walk through life with a deeper and abiding sense of God's presence – and be better equipped to stay connected with Him? Then you are really going to enjoy Belonging.

What about relationships with others?
As we grow our ability to connect with God, Belonging also helps us grow the relational skills needed to help us connect more skillfully with others. Learning to grow our appreciation, our shalom, our brain's relational circuits (RCs) and our Godsight will help us learn to see others – and value them like God does. And, learning to share our shalom and appreciation with others will help them grow the same skills, and empower them to connect in more life-giving relationships.

One of the more exciting elements of Belonging is learning to practice the skills that help us see and value relationships as bigger and more important than the problems. Relationships are always God's priority, and He always sees relationships as bigger and much more important than problems that occur in relationships. When we lose our shalom and appreciation in relationships, we also tend to lose our Godsight – along with some of our brain's best relational functions. We lose the ability to stay connected with others, to be interested in what they think and feel – and to be able to creatively problem solve, resolve conflicts and communicate in ways that are life-giving.

When these things happen, we can no longer see or value other people like God does. At that moment, all we can see are problems – and people as problems. Our highest priority becomes avoiding, eliminating, fixing or solving the problems – or avoiding, eliminating or controlling people who have the problems. We end up making problems bigger and more important than people – and this is not how we want to live.

In Belonging, we'll learn and practice new skills to strengthen our appreciation, shalom, Godsight and RCs so that we'll be better able to stay connected with others, and value them like God does. As we train to make relationships bigger and more important than problems, we'll not only experience less frustration – we'll be empowered to creatively problem solve and partner with others to more easily resolve problems. Relationships will become even more life-giving.

Why Belong?

It seems ironic. You and I are created for relationship, and yet relationships often seem to be the places of greatest hurt, pain and struggle we have. Instead of finding joy, acceptance, delight and strength in relationships, we've encountered rejection, failure, blame and shame. Instead of giving life, our attempts at relationships - particularly with "difficult" people - have left us feeling drained and wondering why we even tried. Yet, there is something deep within us that cries out, "There must be more than what I have experienced in relationships so far!"

For some of us, that voice is loud! We hear it often and yearn for deeper connections with God, family, friends and community. Some of us have a deep longing in our heart for stronger connections and community, but simply don't know how to belong – or know who to belong with. Some of us have vision for community. We've grown significant personal and spiritual maturity, and want to be empowered to build, create and lead deeper and more intentional community for family, spiritual family, friends and those around us. Others of us are wary of community, and protect ourselves by adopting "surface-level" community that lacks intimacy, depth and life-giving

---

RELATIONSHIPS ARE BIGGER AND MORE IMPORTANT THAN PROBLEMS.
One of the more exciting elements of Belonging is learning to practice the skills that help us see and value relationships as bigger and more important than the problems.

relationships. We've settled for the appearance of belonging without any real substance. Some of us have never really felt connected to anyone. We tried hard to make friends and become part of family, friends and spiritual community, and seemed to fail every time. The whole subject of relationships became so painful that we've done our best to avoid it altogether. Our heart's cry for relationship and belonging have grown faint and dim.

If we are honest with ourselves, most of us have struggled at some time or another with belonging. You can probably remember the very awkward moments in school or new settings when people seemed more interested in creating rejection for us than belonging. Instead of acceptance and joy, we found criticism, negativity, and insecurity. Those of us who struggled, didn't seem to fit in easily or were just different became the object of jokes and teasing about the way we looked, dressed, sounded, behaved, played sports or performed in school. People and groups that could have created belonging for us often seemed more preoccupied with using their power to create rejection.

So, in an effort to belong, we learned to perform and jump through whichever "hoops" were needed to be accepted. Belonging was not about joyful acceptance – it was about performance, driven by the kind of insecurity that comes from the fears of failure, inadequacy and rejection. This kind of belonging may have felt better than not belonging at all. But ultimately, this kind of fear and insecurity-driven belonging is an illusion. It drains us – and does not sustain us because it is not life-giving. And unfortunately, if we were one of the few who were able to jump through all of the right hoops and perform well enough to be accepted by the "right" peer group, we often became part of the problem. Instead of creating a joyful place for others to belong, we learned to create fear, insecurity and rejection around us that made it very hard for others to belong.

This is not the kind of "belonging" that we are going to learn in the Belonging module!

What is Belonging?

Simply, Belonging is the joy we create around ourselves. Belonging actively communicates "I am glad you are here" and creates an open invitation for others to be with us. Joy and belonging are contagious invitations to relationship. Belonging is positive – it is creative, resourceful, relational and inventive. It expresses a profound sense of gratitude for others, and for the opportunity to meet, get to know and relate with them. Belonging operates from deep shalom – God's Peace. Belonging is the open, joyful invitation for relationship that we create around us – and allows others to freely respond to us.

In Belonging, we are going to be discovering our unique, God given gifts, talents and abilities to express our own personal style of Belonging to others. Rather than try to jump through a bunch of hoops, we are simply going to focus on learning to build and share our joy with others, and create an open invitation and space for them to relate with us. Each week, you and I are going to learn simple and practical exercises to help us identify and express belonging in our own personal style. You will discover how you can express the characteristics of your heart to others and help them find belonging.

In Belonging, we will also learn a lot of simple and practical relational tools and skills to help us connect with others. We'll learn that belonging works best when we live in appreciation and shalom (God's peace), with the relational circuits (RCs) in our brain fully active. And we'll not only learn to grow appreciation, shalom and RCs – we'll learn how to restore these when they are miss-

---

WHAT IS BELONGING?

Belonging is positive, creative, resourceful, relational, inventive, and actively communicates "I am glad you are here" to create an open invitation for others to be with us.

ing, so that we can reconnect with God and others. We'll learn how to recognize and respond to the kind of pain that prevents belonging – and even learn how to handle our cravings for comfort in ways that are life giving and not destructive. We'll discover how Godsight helps us see people, ourselves and situations from God's perspective.

In addition to these personal relational skills, we'll also discover how to help others stay in appreciation and shalom with their RCs active by not overwhelming them with too much emotional and relational intensity. Overwhelming – or ignoring – others destroys belonging. In Belonging, we'll learn to watch for the signs of overwhelm in ourselves and others, and learn the difference between amplifying distress and ignoring distress so that we can help others stay connected with us.

Everything about Belonging is designed to enhance our relational skills and help us discover our own unique God-given talents and abilities to create a place for others to belong with us – in joy. This is the kind of belonging that Jesus created for others, and it is what we are going to learn and practice.

What do I need to know as we start?

Belonging is Training.
Each week in Belonging, we will learn and practice new exercises that teach the kinds of skills that help us create a joyful place for others to Belong. Please do your best to be there each week. Belonging exercises are progressive and build upon each other. If you miss too many Belonging sessions, it will be hard for you to keep up.

In addition, for you and me to get the most out of our experience in Belonging, we need to practice our skills and exercises during the week. We will have time to learn and practice our new exercises, skills and worksheets in Belonging class – but we are going to need to practice our skills daily at home.

Every week, there will be homework. It's really simple; you are welcome to attend and participate in Belonging – whether you do your homework or not. But you will find your progress and ability to create belonging limited if you do not practice your exercises and skills in homework assignments. Experience has shown that those who are most diligent with their homework in Belonging also tend to make the most progress in Healing, which is the module that follows Belonging.

You will work in "Round Table" groups.
Each week, you will meet with a supportive and encouraging group of people to practice your Belonging skills and learn to practically develop and express belonging in your own personal style. Think about your Round Table members as a group of explorers who are on a belonging journey together. Each of you will be able to give and receive lots of encouragement, and help each other belong – and come back each week.

You will have a Belonging Coordinator to help.
Each Round Table will have a Belonging Coordinator (BC) to help you grow in your belonging skills and help keep your group on track during exercises. Your BC will be learning and practicing Belonging skills along with you, and will be there to encourage all Round Table members on our journey. Your BC will also send you emails during the week to encourage you, create belonging and help remind you of group assignments and homework. Your BC is there to help you, so please let her or him know of any problems or difficulties you are experiencing.

You will help create belonging for members of your Round Table.
Although your BC will encourage all Round Table members, Belonging is designed to help you learn to create belonging and express it to those around you. One of the most practical ways to say "I'm glad you are here" is by learning to encourage and help other Round Table members to return to group each week. Many Belonging exercises, especially in the early weeks, help Round

Table members learn to say "I'm glad you are here and want to see you again next week" by bringing small expressions of appreciation to each other. It is exciting to belong when Round Table members are actively giving and receiving appreciation gifts from each other. You'll find out how to do this in your first week of Belonging.

There are rewards for Belonging.
Each week, your Belonging Facilitator will bring several Belonging gifts to give to class members who do a good job at creating Belonging and helping Round Table members return. Everyone in the class will be able to nominate others for Belonging gifts, and the class will help your Facilitator decide who receives the gifts each week. To help buy these gifts each week, all class members are asked to donate a dollar each week. If you are unable to afford the dollar, don't worry – you still belong and are welcome to participate in Belonging.

Be sure to read "Belonging Goals" and "Wise Thoughts About Group Rules."
These are located immediately after this introductory section of the workbook. The Goals will help you know what you can expect to learn and practice in Belonging. The Wise Thoughts and Guidelines about Group Rules will help you and your group to stay safe and stay on track in Belonging. We will go over these on the first night of class, and be sure to read these over on your own.

You will need your Belonging Workbook for class each week.

Please be sure to bring your Belonging Workbook to every class. Your workbook contains teaching notes, exercise instructions, and weekly worksheets that you will need for in-class exercises as well as homework assignments. You will also need a pen or pencil to complete worksheets and class assignments. In each chapter of your workbook, you will find:

- A complete list of everything that will be covered in your weekly Belonging session.
- Instructions for each weekly exercise.
- Teaching notes from the weekly Belonging DVD lesson.
- All the weekly worksheets and checklists you will need for in-class exercises.
- Weekly homework assignments, including the worksheets.

We will cover one chapter in your workbook each week. The worksheets and checklists you need for each lesson are located at the end of each chapter of your workbook.

In Belonging, you will have the opportunity to participate in many group exercises, and detailed instructions for each of them are included in every chapter of your worksheet. Your facilitator will go over these instructions with you, and your Belonging Coordinator will help you complete many of these exercises. You are welcome to ask questions about anything that is unclear or that you do not understand.

Your workbook also contains teaching notes that accompany each weekly Belonging video. You will find every bit of text seen on the DVD printed in outline form in your workbook. Each page of your workbook also contains space for you to take notes.

At the end of each chapter, you will also find a set of discussion questions. These discussion questions are not for use during the weekly Belonging sessions, but are very useful for personal study. They can also be used in Belonging discussion groups that meet outside of the regularly scheduled Belonging group.

Let's take a look at our Belonging Goals and some Wise Thoughts about Group Rules - and start creating belonging!

BELONGING GOALS:
What Can We Expect to Learn in Belonging?

1. To recognize why belonging is something we create around us.

2. To be part of creating a belonging-friendly environment.

3. To discover my own unique style for creating belonging, and learn to express it!

4. To learn how stories can create belonging – and learn to tell them!

5. To find out how attachment pain stops us from creating belonging, and switches off our Relational Connection Circuits (RCs).

6. To learn to recognize when my RCs are off – and how to turn them back on again – so that I am able to perceive God's presence.

7. To learn belonging skills like appreciation, quieting and telling joyful stories.

8. To perceive God's presence and interact with Him.

9. To discover when attachment pain shuts down belonging.

10. To recognize my cravings – and when they prevent me from creating belonging.

11. To help others keep their RCs on by not overwhelming them – because we know when to stop.

12. To improve maturity skills that help me create more belonging.

13. To learn how my feelings – and learning to express them appropriately – can help create belonging.

14. To spread belonging through our stories.

BELONGING GROUP GUIDELINES:
Ground Rules and Wise Thoughts about Group Rules

1. Help others feel like they belong - create belonging for each other.

2. Express appreciation to each other frequently.

3. Supportive listening helps others share, heal and feel comfortable. It's a lot harder to create belonging and heal when you offer criticism or advice.

4. Encourage others to return to your Round Table – and create belonging for them.

5. Sharing is strongly encouraged, but not required.

6. By following your Facilitator's instructions and the directions in your workbook, you will help keep your group on track, learn new Belonging skills, and help provide enough time for everyone to share.

7. You will learn much more about creating belonging around you if you stay in your Round Table – and do all of your exercises in assigned groups. You are free to talk to your Table Coordinator or Belonging Facilitator about any problems you may encounter.

8. It is very difficult for you and for others to create belonging if you arrive for group intoxicated, so if you come to group under the influence, you won't be able to participate in Belonging that evening.

9. Threats, violence and intimidation are a sign that you are overwhelmed – and are actively and intensely overwhelming others. Because these behaviors make Belonging unsafe for others, you will be unable to return to Belonging if you do them.

10. You create belonging around you and for others when you keep the personal information Belonging members share in group confidential – and do not repeat it to others.

11. You help Belonging members and others stay safe by reporting child or elder abuse – and any imminent danger to the person or property of others.

Belonging
WORKBOOK

FOR USE WITH THE BELONGING DVD SERIES

TWELVE WEEK COURSE WORKBOOK

Belonging Chapter 1:

THE IMMANUEL LIFESTYLE

Group Opens:
- Ask a volunteer to open the group with prayer.

Please start the Belonging DVD for this week's lesson.

Week 1 Teaching Notes: The Belonging Lifestyle

What does "Belonging" look like?
- Belonging is the joy we create around us!

Belonging Can Look Like:
- Bringing a bottle of water to your friend when you pick her up at the airport.
- Moving over with a smile to give someone you don't know a place to sit down.
- Letting up on the gas to let someone merge and then waving or smiling.
- Getting up early to cook your family's breakfast.
- Inviting a new worker or student to join you for lunch.
- Introducing yourself when people move in next door.
- Telling people what you appreciate about them or someone they know.
- Noticing when people make an effort and letting them know you appreciate it.
- Bringing an extra cookie to give away (enough for you and some to share).
- Bringing your wife (or someone else) flowers.
- Praying for the people involved every time you see a problem (like a car accident or something on the news).
- Getting your relational circuits working before you talk about the budget!

Belonging Goals: What do we want to accomplish?
- Recognize why belonging is the joy we create around us.
- Be part of creating a belonging-friendly environment.
- Discover my own unique style for creating belonging – and learn to express it!
- Learn to tell stories that create belonging.
- Build our capacity to live in shalom and appreciation with our brain's relational circuits (RCs) fully active.
- Notice what our body and emotions feel like when we experience shalom and appreciation with our RCs active.
- Discover how we can recognize when shalom and appreciation are missing and our RCs are fading.
- Become skilled at quieting the distress we feel in our body, soul and heart so that we restore shalom, appreciation and our RCs.
- Learn the process of affirmation, and recognize the validation and comfort that help us quiet.
- Become increasingly able to perceive God's presence and interact with Him.
- Find out how attachment pain stops us from creating belonging, and switches off our brain's RCs.
- Practice Godsight, and learn to see myself, others and my situations through God's eyes.
- Learn to recognize my cravings, discover how they prevent me from creating belonging, and find out how I can reduce their intensity.

Notes

- Help others keep their RCs on by not overwhelming them – because we know when to stop.
- Create belonging by learning to recognize the importance of emotions, and the difference between quieting – or dismissing – them.
- Improve maturity skills that help me create more belonging.
- Spread belonging through our stories.
- We can learn these skills together!

Wise thoughts and guidelines: Group Ground Rules
- Help others feel like they belong - create belonging for each other.
- Express appreciation to each other frequently.
- Supportive listening helps others share, heal and feel comfortable. It's a lot harder to create belonging and heal when you offer criticism or advice.
- Encourage others to return to your Round Table – and create belonging for them.
- Sharing is strongly encouraged, but not required.
- By following your facilitator's instructions and the directions in your workbook, you will help keep your group on track, learn new Belonging skills, and help provide enough time for everyone to share.
- You will learn much more about creating belonging around you if you stay in your Round Table – and do all of your exercises in assigned groups. You are free to talk to your Table Coordinator or Belonging Facilitator about any problems you may encounter.
- It is very difficult for you and for others to create belonging if you arrive for group intoxicated, so if you come to group under the influence, you won't be able to participate in Belonging that evening.
- Threats, violence and intimidation are a sign that you are overwhelmed and are actively and intensely overwhelming others. Because these behaviors make Belonging unsafe for others, you will be unable to return to Belonging if you do them.
- You create belonging around you and for others when you keep the personal information Belonging members share in group confidential – and do not repeat it to others.
- You help Belonging members and others stay safe by reporting child or elder abuse – and any imminent danger to the person or property of others.

What is Belonging?
- And what kinds of things are important as we get started tonight and form our Belonging Groups?

What does "Belonging" look like?
- Belonging is the joy we create around us!

Weekly Bible Story: Belonging is the Immanuel Lifestyle
- The story of Jesus at Simon's House, Luke 7:36-50.

Belonging is training!

Belonging has a combination of weekly class exercises, teaching and homework to help you learn to create and express belonging with your own personal style.

Belonging will help you learn how to create and express belonging to people around you – in your own style.

BELONGING IS TRAINING!
Coming to Belonging without practicing the exercises and doing homework is a lot like trying to build muscle by reading exercise books...but never actually working out!

- Each week, you'll have the chance to practice in class with the members of your Belonging Round Table.

What kind of things will help us get started and form our Round Tables? What is a Belonging Round Table?
- Each week, you and the same small group of Belonging members will meet around a table during class for exercises to practice new skills that will help you learn to create and experience belonging together.

Round Table formation tips
- Diversity is very valuable.
- Change usually means learning to do things we've never done before...even if it feels a little bit uncomfortable.
- Commitment to attend is vital.
- Many of our Belonging Activities involve learning to help each other to return, and rewarding those who help others.
- Learning is very important.
- Learning to build community is much more important than learning information about community.

Couples
- You may stay together if you both want to.
- You may find that it is sometimes easier to train in separate groups.

Healthy 3 Way Bonds
- These bonds can be very dynamic.
- You may be very comfortable with each other and want to learn how to help others belong around us.
- You may want to help a person who feels like he or she doesn't belong and is a little bit anxious.

You may find that you get "triggered" by something in Belonging. If this happens, do your best to:
- Work on restoring your relational circuits (more about this later)
- Stay teachable and humble

Round Table formation tips: We are all different!
- Some of us will have different understandings of what Belonging is – and what we want to learn in Belonging.
- Some of us have been through Forming, some through Restarting – and maybe some through neither group.

Belonging has rewards!
- Each week, we'll each put $1.00 in a pot to buy appreciation gifts for class members that best help create belonging for others. (See page 7).
- We'll use it to reward the people and groups that best help create belonging for others!

Let's get started!
- Follow your facilitator's instructions as you start your first Belonging exercise and join your Round Table.

LEARNING NEW INFORMATION IS IMPORTANT, BUT:

Learning to apply the skills we need to create a joyful place for others to belong with us is much, much more important than studying new information about belonging.

Notes

Belonging Exercise: Forming your Round Table

Follow your facilitator's instructions as she or he guides you through this exercise. You will have 35 minutes.

1. Stand and move to the front of the room to get a Belonging name tag. Fill it out and put it on.
   a. While you are up front, put a dollar in the pot. Your facilitator will show you where it's located.
   b. When you are finished, please remain standing.
2. Follow your facilitator's instructions as you:
   a. Form groups of 3 people with anyone you want.
   b. Your facilitator will pass out your official Belonging string. Each person in your group of 3 should hold one end. When all 3 ends of a group's string are taken, that group cannot add new members.
3. Remain in your group and locate the Belonging Group Similarity Form on page 18 of your workbook. Complete this form as a group, and when you are finished, wait for more instructions from your facilitator.
4. When all groups have completed their form, your facilitator will let you know that it's time to move on to the next step in the exercise.
5. Now, use the totals from your worksheet to find another group of 3 that is the most different from yours. You are now forming groups of 6.
6. Remain standing with your new group of 6 as your facilitator helps adjust groups as needed. Please be patient!
7. When adjustments are complete, your facilitator will appoint a Belonging Coordinator (BC) for each group.
8. Now, your new group can find a table and sit down together with your BC. This is your new Round Table, and you should sit together each week.

Belonging Exercise: Expressing my own style of creating Belonging to others

You will have 20 minutes for this Round Table exercise.

1. Remain in your Round Tables for this exercise, and your facilitator will keep track of time for you.
2. Start by completing your Belonging Contact Information Form on page 19.
   a. Your BC will complete this form for your Round Table and email you a copy this week.
   b. This info will help you stay in touch with each other, and is not to be shared outside of Belonging.
3. As you complete your form, your facilitator will assign a number to each Round Table. You'll need this number for future exercises.
4. You will have 5 minutes to finish this part of the exercise.
5. When you have finished, form small groups of 3 with other Round Table Members, and get ready to answer this question: What would you do if you wanted someone to:
   a. Call you again,
   b. Come back to see you,
   c. Help you return next week?
6. Share your answers and try your favorite belonging style with the other 2 members of your small group. You can try things like:
   a. Smiling
   b. Complimenting them
   c. Learning their names

Notes

    d. Finding a mutual interest
    e. Asking them to come back
    f. What else can you think of?

7. You will have 10 minutes for this part of the exercise. Return to your Round Table when you are finished.

Belonging exercise: What kind of appreciation gifts would you like in this class?

You will have 5 minutes for this exercise.

1. This is a class discussion to help answer the question: How would you like to reward people who do a great job at creating belonging?

2. Your facilitator will lead this discussion and make a class list with your suggestions.

3. Volunteers can make suggestions!
    a. These are the kinds of gifts your facilitator will buy with the money you put into the Belonging pot each week to express appreciation to class members who do a good job expressing belonging.
    b. Your facilitator will bring 2-3 gifts for class next week using the funds in the Belonging pot.
    c. Next week, you will help decide who has done the best job of creating belonging for the week – and who receives the appreciation gifts.
    d. Listen as your facilitator helps you think about the kind of gifts that are appropriate.

Belonging Homework: Week 1

Belonging Coordinators:

- Send everyone in your Round Table an email welcoming them to Belonging.
- Include a copy of the Belonging Contact Information Worksheet in your email, page 19.

Everyone:

- Experiment with how you might like to create belonging by bringing an appreciation gift for your Round Table Belonging Coordinator next week.

Instructions:

1. Pick an item from the following list.

2. Leave it on a chair at your Round Table for your Coordinator when you arrive next week.

3. Think about things like:
    a. A blessing card you made – or bought if needed.
    b. Bring a snack you like to share for the BC.
    c. Give the Coordinator a flower.
    d. Give the Coordinator a "Gold Star" for something you appreciate about him or her.

4. You can also make a coupon your BC can redeem for:
    a. Something you'll pray about for your Coordinator.
    b. Anything free or less than $1 that makes your Coordinator feel special.
    c. A one minute neck rub.
    d. A fresh fruit of her or his choice next week.
    e. Something you think of or create on your own!

Notes

Belonging Group Similarity Form

Copyright E. James Wilder Ph.D. and Ed Khouri, 2009

You will need this worksheet to complete the Round Table Formation Exercise. Your facilitator will guide you through this exercise, so be sure to follow your facilitator's directions and work with your group of 3 to complete this worksheet.

Circle the number of group members who:

A. 0 1 (2) 3 Attended Forming.

B. (0) 1 2 3 Attended Restarting.

C. 0 1 (2) 3 See each other at church.

D. (0) 1 2 3 Attend the same activities outside Belonging.

E. (0) 1 2 3 Are part of the same natural family.

F. 0 1 2 (3) Are within 10 years of the same age.

G. (0) 1 2 3 Have one or less friends you know well in the room.

H. 0 (1) 2 3 Have difficulty experiencing God's presence when you try.

I. (0) 1 2 3 Relate to God more easily than to people.

J. 0 (1) 2 3 Usually become leaders when you are in a group.

K. 0 (1) 2 3 Have a gift of hospitality.

L. 0 (1) 2 3 Have read the Life Model or attended a THRIVE conference.

M. (0) 1 2 3 Genuinely enjoy the presence of Chihuahuas.

N. 0 (1) 2 3 Genuinely enjoy the presence of cats.

O. 0 1 2 (3) Believe that silliness is a form of art.

_____

15 Count (or estimate) how many weeks of Forming experience are in your group.
    Count one week for every person attending. The total will be between 0 and 36.

0 Count (or estimate) how many weeks of Restarting experience are in your group.
    Count one week for every person attending. The total will be between 0 and 36.

Coordinators: Belonging Contact Information Form

Providing this information will make it possible for your Round Table members and Coordinator to stay in touch. Listing your name and email address will help your Coordinator send you updates – and help you to create belonging around you! Your Belonging Coordinator will provide copies of this form for all group members at our next session. This information will not be shared with anyone outside of Belonging.

Name	Email	Phone

Belonging Facilitator and Belonging Coordinator Contact Information Form

It is important for the Belonging Facilitator and Belonging Coordinators to stay in touch with each other. Use this form in your first Facilitator – Coordinator meeting to share your names, phone numbers and email addresses with each other. To help your group complete Belonging exercises, you will sometimes need to share information with each other, so be sure to list email addresses and phone numbers that you check regularly. If needed, your Belonging Facilitator will make copies or email the contact information to each Belonging Coordinator.

Name	Email	Phone

Chapter 1: Questions for Further Discussion

1. Imagine that you are present at the house of Simon the Pharisee when Jesus comes to dinner. Which of the following characters in this story do you most closely identify with? Why?
   a. Simon.
   b. Jesus.
   c. The woman.
   d. The crowd watching from outside.
   e. Simon's friends watching from the inside.

2. What does "belonging" mean to you? How is the definition of "belonging" used in this week's lesson different from the way you've understood it before?

3. Why is Belonging "training?" When will you schedule time each week to complete your Belonging assignments?

4. How do you like to create belonging? What would you do if you wanted someone to: call you again, come back to see you, or help you return next week?

5. What kinds of experiences have you had with creating belonging over time? Take a look at your personal belonging history, and answer these questions:
   a. How did you create belonging - or belong - when you were in Grade School, High School, and College?
   b. When you were growing up, how did you create belonging with friends? How do you create belonging with friends now?
   c. How did you experience and create belonging in your family when you were growing up? How do you experience and create belonging in your family or home now?
   d. How did you create and experience belonging in dating relationships? How do you create and experience belonging with your spouse, boyfriend/girlfriend or significant others now?
   e. What did you learn and experience about belonging at church growing up? How do you create and experience belonging at church now?
   f. How do you create and experience belonging at work?

6. If you could change anything about how you create and experience belonging now, what would it be?

7. After our first session of Belonging, what Belonging goals would you like to accomplish as part of this class?

Notes

Belonging Chapter 2:

CAN BELONGING REALLY BE THIS SIMPLE?

Group Opens:
• Ask a volunteer to open the group with prayer.

Adding new members to Round Tables:

• What is Belonging? What kinds of things are important as we get started tonight and form our Belonging Groups?
• Because some new people may have joined Belonging this week, your facilitator may need to add a few new people to your Round Table, and review important Belonging principles, wise thoughts, guidelines and group ground rules.
• Your facilitator will also add new members to Round Tables as needed.

Please start the Belonging DVD for this week's lesson.

What does "Belonging" look like?
• Belonging is the joy we create around us!

Belonging is Training!

Wise thoughts and guidelines: Group Ground Rules
• Help others feel like they belong - create belonging for each other.
• Express appreciation to each other frequently.
• Supportive listening helps others share, heal and feel comfortable. It's a lot harder to create belonging and heal when you offer criticism or advice.
• Encourage others to return to your Round Table – and create belonging for them.
• Sharing is strongly encouraged, but not required.
• By following your facilitator's instructions and the directions in your workbook, you will help keep your group on track, learn new Belonging skills, and help provide enough time for everyone to share.
• You will learn much more about creating belonging around you if you stay in your Round Table – and do all of your exercises in assigned groups. You are free to talk to your Table Coordinator or Belonging Facilitator about any problems you may encounter.
• It is very difficult for you and for others to create belonging if you arrive for group intoxicated, so if you come to group under the influence, you won't be able to participate in Belonging that evening.
• Threats, violence and intimidation are a sign that you are overwhelmed and are actively and intensely overwhelming others. Because these behaviors make Belonging unsafe for others, you will be unable to return to Belonging if you do them.
• You create belonging around you and for others when you keep the personal information Belonging members share in group confidential – and do not repeat it to others.
• You help Belonging members and others stay safe by reporting child or elder abuse – and any imminent danger to the person or property of others.

Pause the DVD for Belonging Class Exercises
When the exercises are complete, please restart the DVD.

Notes

Belonging Exercises: Finding & expressing "my own style" of creating belonging to others

Exercise Introduction:
- What do you do or give to others so they will be glad to see you – or want to come back?
- Here are a few Belonging ideas!

Belonging ideas: Belonging is not expensive:
- Prayer.
- Phone calls or emails.
- Arrive at class early to welcome others.
- Accountability, anticipation, partnerships.
- Tell someone an appreciation story.
- Your Belonging Contact Information Form may be helpful.

You can also make or buy simple belonging gifts that are free, easy to find or cost less than $1.
- Cards or personal notes.
- Scripture verses that you found this week.
- A special treat for the Round Table.
- Think about bringing a few flowers to put on another Round Table.
- Creatively decorate a Round Table.

Exercise Instructions: Part 1
You will have 10 minutes for this part of the exercise

1. Follow your facilitator's instructions as you move through each part of this exercise.

2. Form groups of 3 from your Round Table and answer the following question: What do you do for others – or give to others – so they will be glad to see you or want to come back?

3. Remember the suggestions we've made – or create your own style of belonging!

4. You will have 10 minutes, and your facilitator will keep track of time for you.

Exercise Instructions: Part 2
You will have 10 minutes for this part of the exercise

1. Return to your Round Tables for this part of the exercise.

2. In three words, tell your Round Table what you like to do or give to someone so they know you are "glad they are there."

3. Anything you give must be free or less than $1.

4. Your Belonging Coordinator will write these down using the "Three ways everyone likes to give Belonging at my Round Table" form on page 37.

5. You will have 10 minutes, and your facilitator will keep track of time for you.

Belonging Exercise: Appreciation Gifts
You will have 5 minutes for this exercise.

1. Remain at your Round Table while your facilitator leads this exercise and asks for your help in deciding who should receive this week's Belonging appreciation gifts. These are the gifts you discussed in last week's class, and were purchased with the dollar each person put in the Belonging pot last week.

2. Your facilitator will ask you to nominate classmates who did a great job creating and expressing belonging in class this week.

3. Those who did a really good job will receive applause and appreciation from the class.

4. Your facilitator – with your help – will determine who receives this week's Belonging appreciation gifts.

Please restart the Belonging DVD.

Belonging Teaching Notes: Can belonging skills really be this simple?

- Learning and growing skills to create joyful belonging around me.

Weekly Bible Story: Why do we stop creating belonging?
- The Fall of the Superhero: Uriah and David.

Appreciation, Shalom and Belonging.

Phil 4:8:
- Finally, brethren, whatever is true, whatever is honorable, whatever is just, whatever is pure, whatever is lovely, whatever is gracious, if there is any excellence, if there is anything worthy of praise, think about these things. (RSV)

Shalom
- Everything is in the right relationship,
- In the right place,
- At the right strength,
- And the right amount,
- For God and people.
- Synchronized

In Shalom, we build belonging around us for:
- Plants.
- Animals.
- Nature.
- People.
- Spiritual Family.

When my brain and spirit are in shalom, I am:
- Open.
- Interested.
- Flexible.
- Self-reflective.
- Using all my senses.

I work to have other people close to me, and we appreciate each other!

Appreciation is a sign of shalom!

Appreciation feels like:
- A reunion with someone I've missed.
- Cuddling or a warm blanket.
- Watching a baby sleep or a happy hug.
- A cozy breakfast or a cabin in the woods.

> ### WHAT IS SHALOM?
> *Shalom means that everything is in the right relationship, in the right place, at the right strength and amount for God and people. Shalom is much more than an "absence of conflict." In Shalom, we are synchronized (in tune) together with God and others. Appreciation is a sign of shalom, and telling appreciation stories spreads our Shalom.*

- A gorgeous view
- I feel like I belong!

What does appreciation feel like to you?
- What emotions do you feel if you lose appreciation – or can't find it at all?

Pause the DVD for a class exercise.

Belonging Exercise: What does appreciation feel like to you, and what does it feel like when you've lost it?

This is a 5 minute exercise. When it is finished, please restart the DVD.

1. Remain at your Round Table and follow your facilitator's instructions for this class exercise.

2. As a class, share answers to these questions on your "What does appreciation feel like to me?" Worksheet, page 31.
    a. What does appreciation feel like to you?
    b. What emotions do you feel if you lose appreciation – or can't find it at all?

3. Write any answers that apply to you in the space provided.

4. You will have 5 Minutes, and when you are finished, please restart the DVD.

Please restart the Belonging DVD.

My body feels appreciation too!
- My skin feels warm.
- My stomach is settled.
- A smile on my face.
- Cozy and welcoming.
- Lighter.
- Restful.
- Sheltered.
- I want to create belonging!

What does your body feel like when you feel appreciation?
- What happens in your body when you lose your appreciation – or don't feel it at all?

Pause the DVD for a class exercise.

Belonging Exercise: What does your body feel like when you feel appreciation, and what does your body feel like when you've lost it?

This is a 5 minute exercise. When it is finished, please restart the DVD

1. Remain at your Round Table and follow your facilitator's instructions for this class exercise.

2. As a class, share answers to these questions on your "What does appreciation feel like to me?" worksheet, page 31.
    a. What does your body feel like when you feel appreciation?
    b. What happens in your body when you lose your appreciation – or don't feel it at all?

3. Write any answers that apply to you in the space provided.

4. You will have 5 Minutes, and when you are finished, please restart the DVD.

Please restart the Belonging DVD.

When we live in appreciation and shalom, our brains – and our relationships – work best.
- Appreciation and shalom help our brain's Relational Circuits (RCs) come alive, and our relationships are life-giving.

Living in shalom and appreciation with our brain's relational circuits fully alive is how we thrive!
- It's where we want to live!
- It's also how we create belonging around us for others.

This is why:
- Growing our capacity for shalom and appreciation, and
- Learning to notice when we are living in shalom and appreciation – with our RCs fully active,
- Are essential goals in Belonging!

Learning to tell appreciation stories is a great way to grow appreciation.

Sharing my appreciation stories spreads shalom and appreciation.
- Sharing gratitude creates belonging for all of us.

Appreciation is contagious:
- The more I think about the people and moments I appreciate, the more appreciation I experience.
- When I learn to share these stories with you, appreciation multiplies in both of us.

Good appreciation stories build appreciation, because they include you!

Sharing appreciation stories helps me remember them.
- It's a good idea to tell God the story first, because He loves to hear our stories.
- Sharing our stories shows our appreciation to God, and helps others share gratitude with us.

Remembering and sharing my stories changes my brain.
- The more I focus my attention on appreciation, the more I tend to find and notice things I appreciate.
- Remembering and sharing creates a new expectancy in my thinking, and before long, I'm looking for new things to appreciate.

Let's learn how to tell stories that build shalom, appreciation and belonging!

A good shalom and appreciation story:
- Has everything in the right place at the right time for others to share your experience with you.
- We call these 4+Stories because you need the 4 parts of the control center in the right hemisphere of your brain, plus the words and explanations from the left hemisphere, to tell the story.
- When we have appreciation and shalom inside, and we tell our stories the 4+ way, we create the opening for our listeners to belong there with us.

That sounds really complicated!
- How can I get started and learn to tell a 4+ Appreciation and Shalom Story?

Getting ready to tell our stories and the appreciation story exercise:
- We want to notice and tell stories about people and experiences that we appreciate.

WHY ARE APPRECIATION STORIES IMPORTANT?

Learning to tell appreciation stories the 4+ way helps spread shalom and appreciation around us - and helps us create belonging. Remembering and sharing my stories changes how my brain works. Focusing my attention on appreciation creates a sense of hopeful expectancy in me, and before long, I am finding new things to appreciate!

Notes

- Start thinking about moments in your life when you felt a strong sense of appreciation and gratitude for someone.

For example, think about times when:
- Someone was kind to you, helped you when they didn't have to, gave you a special gift – or created a place for you to belong.
- You felt very close to someone who treated you with dignity, respect, friendship and compassion.
- Something funny made you both laugh out loud.
- You saw a beautiful sunset, shared a smile or played with your favorite pet together.
- These are the kinds of things we want to remember!

Use your Appreciation Worksheet to guide you:
- The worksheet will help you include all the elements that help your story spread shalom and appreciation – and build belonging around you.
- Your Appreciation Story worksheet is located at the end of chapter 2 in your workbook.

Choosing my story
- Start by choosing a story that has a moderate feeling level, and is not too intense.
- Be sure that you can talk freely about your story, and do not have to be guarded in telling it.

People and details:
- Write the name of the person you appreciate, and briefly list the details for your story.
- Who do you appreciate?
- What happened?
- What did you appreciate?
- Why?

Building my story:
- What does appreciation feel like emotionally and physically?
  o Select words that best describe the emotions you felt before and after your appreciation experience.
  o Choose the words that best describe how your body felt before and after your experience.
- What did you appreciate and how does it feel?
  o List 3 things you appreciate about what the person you are describing did for you.
  o Choose the words that best describe what appreciation feels like to you.

Remember: To best describe how appreciation feels to you emotionally and physically:
- You can choose words from the list on the Appreciation Story worksheet.
- You can also use any of the words you wrote on the "What does appreciation feel like to me" worksheet during today's class discussion.

Finishing my story
- In the last section of your worksheet, choose words to describe how the feeling of appreciation affects your desire to create belonging.

Now, complete the "Telling my story the 4+ way" checklist

IN BELONGING WE WANT TO GROW OUR APPRECIATION!
We are going to practice telling appreciation stories throughout our Belonging class. Today, practice telling stories using your 4+ Shalom Stories with Appreciation Worksheet in class. For homework, be sure to prepare another story to share next week.

- Your facilitator will show you how to complete the checklist, and how you can use it to encourage each other as you tell your stories.

Now tell your story!
- Break into small groups of 3 with other members of your Round Table.
- Your facilitator will keep track of time for you throughout each part of the exercise.
- Each of you will have 3 minutes to tell your story to your Round Table.
- When your story is complete, you will have 2 minutes to ask for feedback.
- Your small group will encourage you for every element of the story that you were able to include.

Let's tell some stories!

Belonging exercise: Telling my 4+ Appreciation Story
You will have 25 minutes for this exercise, and your facilitator will keep track of time for you. This exercise will help you learn to tell a 4+ Appreciation Story that builds joy, spreads shalom and creates belonging.

Exercise Instructions

1. To start, remain at your Round Tables for instructions.

2. Listen as your facilitator tells you a 4+ Appreciation Story and notice how each element of an appreciation story is included.
   a. Follow along using your Appreciation Story Worksheet, page 35.
   b. Afterwards, your facilitator will ask you for feedback to see if all the elements were included in the story. Encourage your facilitator for each element he or she included.
   c. Pay attention to feedback!
   d. Pay close attention to how they ask for feedback, and to the encouragement they receive, because you will be using the same process, after your stories.
   e. You are about to start telling stories!

3. Form groups of 3 with other members of your Round Table. You will be sharing your stories in these small groups.

4. Fill out your worksheet, pages 32-24. You will have 5 minutes, and your facilitator will keep track of time for you.

5. Telling your story
   a. All members of your small group will have 3 minutes to tell their story.
   b. After your story, take 2 minutes to ask for feedback. Encourage each other for every element included in the story.
   c. Your facilitator will keep track of time for you.

6. When listening to a story
   a. Create belonging for the storytellers by looking at them and making appropriate eye contact as they tell a story.
   b. Listen for each element of a 4+ Appreciation Story, and notice how they include each element in the story.

7. When giving feedback:
   a. Be positive and encouraging.
   b. Be sure you limit feedback to helping storytellers recognize how they included the elements of a 4+ Appreciation Story as listed on the worksheet.

Belonging Assignment: Collect appreciation moments
- Find more appreciation moments this week, and list them in the "Assignment for Belonging Week 2: Collect more appreciation moments" section of your 4+ Appreciation Story Worksheet, page 34.
- You will need this list and the 4+ Shalom Story Appreciation Worksheet for homework.

Notes

Belonging Homework: Week 2

Belonging Coordinators:
- Send an email to all Round Table Members and include the list of how each member expressed belonging to you, and thank everyone for their gift. Use the worksheet on page 36.
- Send an email to your facilitator, other coordinators and members of your Round Table and include the list of the 3 ways everyone likes to give belonging in your group. Use the worksheet on page 37.

Everyone: All Round Table members: Create belonging!
- Prepare a way you like to create belonging for the 2 other members of the small group you were in at the beginning of class.
- If there were more than 3 in your group, make enough for each one in your little group.
- You can use ideas from Weeks 1 or 2, or create something new, but it must be free or under $1.

Everyone: Collect Appreciation Moments:
- Instructions:
    - o Your assignment is located on the bottom of page 34, just before your Appreciation Story Worksheet.
    - o Make a list of other appreciation moments you notice this week.
    - o Bring your list to class next week, because you will need it to tell an appreciation story!

Notes

What Does Appreciation Feel Like to Me?

©Copyright E. James Wilder Ph.D. and Ed Khouri, 2009.

Use this worksheet to write down the lists of words to describe appreciation that are suggested in class. Our goal is to identify for ourselves what appreciation feels like to us and to our body. We also want to identify what it feels like emotionally and what happens in our body when we lose appreciation – or can't find it anywhere!

We will use these words to tell appreciation stories in class, and to help recognize the times when we are experiencing Shalom and are ready to create belonging. Our stories will also help us remember other relationships, times and places in which we experienced appreciation and a strong sense of belonging. This list of words can also help us better identify what it feels like when we are not able to create belonging and need to return to appreciation and shalom.

To me, appreciation feels like:

When I lose appreciation – or can't find it at all – I feel these emotions:

When I feel appreciation, my body feels:

When I lose appreciation – or can't find it at all – my body feels:

Notes

Appreciation Story Worksheet
©Copyright E. James Wilder Ph.D. and Ed Khouri, 2009.

Philippians 4:8 Finally, brethren, whatever is true, whatever is honorable, whatever is just, whatever is pure, whatever is lovely, whatever is gracious, if there is any excellence, if there is anything worthy of praise, think about these things.

Stories Create Belonging around Me and Spread Shalom

Shalom is a Hebrew word that means everything is in the right relationship, at the right time, in the right place, at the right strength and in the right amount for God and people. In the Life Model we call this being synchronized. In Shalom we build belonging around us for plants, animals, nature, people and spiritual family. With the best of our brain and spirit in Shalom we are open, self-reflective, interested, flexible, and use all our senses. We work to have other people close to us and we appreciate each other.

When I start to feel Shalom, a vital sign is appreciation. Appreciation feels like finally finding someone I have waited anxiously to see for a long time. Appreciation is like a reunion, cuddling, a warm blanket, a cozy breakfast, a cabin in the woods, watching a baby sleep, a gorgeous view or a happy hug from your grandchild. I feel like belonging here.

When I feel appreciation, my skin feels warm, my stomach settles, my shoulders relax, or maybe a little smile plays on my face. I feel lighter, cozy, welcoming, hopeful, restful and sheltered. I am ready to enjoy my food, my surroundings, my companions, my activities and my rest. I want to create belonging here.

Appreciation also opens up the past and I remember the good moments, the kind times, the times God and loving people created belonging. Appreciation makes me think of many ways to create belonging, enjoy belonging, share belonging and "pay it forward."

My brain will always store my appreciation memory, but I may not be able to find where my brain stored the memory unless I tell appreciation stories. Telling stories makes sure that my mind puts my appreciation where I can find it again. It is a good idea to tell the story to God first just for practice and out of respect. Telling the story to others shows appreciation to God -which is always a good idea. Telling the appreciation story creates belonging around me.

Appreciation Story Exercise

In this exercise we want to notice and tell stories about someone we appreciate. Start by thinking about people you appreciate, especially if they have created a place for you to belong, or if you have created a place for them to belong. We are going to remember how those moments of appreciation affected you, and turn one into a story to help spread shalom, appreciation and belonging around you.

It is surprising how many people only use their ability to create belonging when they want to use you, get you in the same trouble they are in, sell you something or make a conquest. Some belonging stories have very mixed messages, because the person who created belonging both helped you and used you. We will not tell these stories today. Start by writing down some ideas, even if you don't remember names.

Name	What do I appreciate about this person?

Building my appreciation story

A good Shalom story has everything in the right place and the right amount for others to share the experience with you. We call these stories 4+ stories because to tell them you need the four parts of your right brain plus the words and explanations from your left brain to tell the story. With all the parts working together we have Shalom inside, and we create the opening for our listeners to belong there with us.

Notes

Choosing the right story
- ❑ This story has a moderate feeling level and is not too intense.
- ❑ I do not need to be guarded about this story and can talk freely about it.

Choose the details: Briefly describe what this person did that you appreciate

Tell how my body felt before and after the appreciation. (Pick words or add your own.)

Before	Tight	Shaky	Heart pounding
	Numb	Heavy	A sad look on my face
	Head pounding	Like curling up inside	Sick
After	Lighter	Warm inside	Calmer
	A smile on my face	Energized	Relaxed

Include emotion words describing how I felt before and after the appreciation. (Pick words or add your own.)

Before	Lonely	Afraid	Separate	Shy
	Homesick	Lost	Like crying	Confused
	Distant	Hurt	Like hiding	Like I don't fit
After	Relieved	Happy	Peaceful	Settled
	Hopeful	Like I belonged	At home	Thankful
	Less alone	Freer	Ready to try again	Understood

What I really appreciate that (name) did for me: (list three things or more)

1.	
2.	
3.	
4.	

When I feel appreciation: (pick words or add your own)

My skin feels warm	I feel welcomed	I feel sheltered	I feel OK
It feels cozy	It feels safe	It's like a warm blanket	It's like giving a hug
I feel deep satisfaction	I feel a smile inside	I feel understood	I feel valued

I want to create belonging and: (How do I want to create belonging-act like myself again)

Give back	Thank them	Do something for them
Do the same thing for others	Go visit them again if I could	Teach the world to sing
Make someone smile	Thank God	Send a card
Give them a gift	Tell this story again	Learn to be that way too

Notes

Telling my story the 4+ way
- ❑ This story is about me (autobiographical) and I am involved in telling the story.
- ❑ I show genuine emotions on my face and in my voice when telling the story.
- ❑ I keep eye contact with my listeners while storytelling.
- ❑ I include words for my emotions.
- ❑ I describe what my body felt like.
- ❑ I describe appreciation enough for others to know how it feels.
- ❑ I say what it is like me to do when I am creating belonging once again.
- ❑ This story begins and ends with my feeling appreciation.

Tell your story now to your round table.
(You may need to be in groups of 3 people).

You could start this way:
- "I would like to thank (name)" and express how I appreciated what he/she did.
- Tell what the person did that you appreciate.
- Use feeling words.
- Tell your body sensations before and after.
- Tell how appreciation felt.
- Say how that inspires you to create belonging around you.

Group Encouragement:
The round table (or your group of 3) will check for the characteristics of Telling my story the 4+ way and give you encouragement about all the ones you were able to include.

Assignment for Belonging Week Two: Collect more appreciation moments

We have many appreciation moments in our lives besides elders. A beautiful scene in nature is part of God creating belonging for you! There are moments that we just say "Ahh!" and "Oh" and "That is beautiful!" "I wish I had a camera," I always want to remember this," "That was so sweet!" "Thank you so much!" and those moments of appreciation restart our desire to create belonging around us. The desire to create belonging will soon fade unless we tell the story of appreciation to someone. We will also forget to create belonging unless we remember these times of appreciation.

Notice any appreciation moments this week. Put them on a list and tell them as a story. Think back over your life and add more appreciation moments to your library. These are God's gifts. Give the appreciation moment a clearer but short name like, "By Lake Superior" that reminds you of that story.

Name for Appreciation Moment	Short description to remind me what I appreciated

Notes

Belonging 4+ Shalom Story with Appreciation Worksheet

Telling my appreciation story the 4+ way
- ❑ This story has a moderate feeling level and is not too intense.
- ❑ I do not need to be guarded about this story and can talk freely about it.
- ❑ This story is about me (autobiographical) and I am involved in telling the story.
- ❑ I show genuine emotions on my face and in my voice when telling the story.
- ❑ I keep eye contact with my listeners while storytelling.
- ❑ I include words for my emotions.
- ❑ I describe what my body felt like.
- ❑ I describe appreciation enough for others to know how it feels.
- ❑ I say what it is like me to do when I am creating belonging once again.
- ❑ This story begins and ends with my feeling appreciation.

Give a brief description of my situation:

Use these emotional feeling words for my story:

Include this description of how my body felt:

Say what I appreciated:

Tell the effect of appreciation on my desire to create belonging (share good things with others)

Coordinators: How Did my Round Table Express Belonging to Me?
©Copyright E. James Wilder Ph.D. and Ed Khouri, 2009.

Instructions: This week, your Round Table members brought you an appreciation gift to express their personal style of creating belonging. Use this form to list the name of everyone who brought you an expression of belonging. Save this form; you'll need it again in Week 5.

This week, send an email to everyone on this list and express your appreciation to them!

Name	Belonging Expression

Coordinators: 3 Ways Everyone at my Round Table Likes to Give Belonging to Others.
©Copyright E. James Wilder Ph.D. and Ed Khouri, 2009.

Instructions: This week, Round Table members will be asked to share their favorite ways of giving the gift of belonging to others. Each will give you 3 words to describe what they like to do or give so that others will know "'I'm glad you are here." Write each of these words down. Save this form; you'll need it again in Week 5.

This week, you will email your list to everyone in your Round Table.

Name	Give Belonging 1		Give Belonging 2		Give Belonging 3

Notes

Chapter 2: Questions for Further Discussion

√1. Why do you stop creating belonging? Can you remember a time that you used to create belonging and then stopped? What happened? Were you able to start creating belonging again?

2. Could you relate to the story of King David, his cravings, and his loss of appreciation and belonging? What happens to your ability to create belonging when cravings increase, and you lose appreciation?

3. What does appreciation feel like to you:
Emotionally?
In your body?

4. What do you feel when you've lost appreciation - or can't find it anywhere?
Emotionally?
In your body?

5. Do you think of yourself as a person who experiences appreciation or gratitude often? What kinds of people or situations bring you appreciation? On a regular day, how much time do you spend feeling appreciation?

6. How would you describe shalom? What does it mean to you?

7. How did you feel when you told your appreciation story to your small group? How did it feel to listen as others shared their stories with you? Do appreciation stories grow your sense of appreciation? Why - or why not?

√ 8. For the next week, find at least one person, event or situation to appreciate each day. List each appreciation moment, and describe what that moment felt like to you emotionally and in your body. Does it get easier to find and experience appreciation as the week goes on?

Notes

Notes

Belonging Chapter 3:

WIRED FOR RELATIONSHIP:
DISCOVERING MY BRAIN'S RELATIONAL CIRCUITS.

Group Opens:
- Ask a volunteer to open the group with prayer.

Belonging Exercise: Creating Belonging
You will have 25 minutes for this exercise.

Part 1: Gather in groups of 3

1. Gather in your groups of 3 from last week, and give the other 2 members of your small group your expression of how you like to create belonging with them.

2. Express appreciation to each other.

3. You will have 5 minutes, and your facilitator will keep track of time for you.

Part 2: Remain in your groups of 3

1. Stay in your small groups and answer: What do you like to receive from others to make you feel at home, remembered or appreciated?

2. Focus on styles of relating, response and gifts that are free, easy to find or cost less than $1.

3. You will have 10 minutes, and you facilitator will keep track of time for you.

Part 3: Return to your Round Tables

1. In 3 words, share what you like to receive to feel someone is "glad you are there" that are free or less than $1.

2. Your Belonging Coordinator will write these on the "Three ways everyone at my Round Table likes to receive belonging from others" form, page 47.

3. You will have 10 minutes.

Belonging exercise: Appreciation Stories
You will have 24 minutes for this exercise

1. Remain at your Round Tables as your facilitator introduces this exercise and reviews 4+ Appreciation Stories with you.
   a. Sharing my appreciation stories spreads shalom and appreciation.
   b. Sharing gratitude creates belonging for all of us.
   c. When we have appreciation and shalom inside, and we tell our stories the 4+ way, we create the opening for our listeners to belong there with us.
   d. A good shalom and appreciation story:
      I. Has everything in the right place at the right time for others to share your experience with you.
      II. We call these 4+ Stories because you need the 4 parts of the control center in the right hemisphere of your brain plus the words and explanations from the left hemisphere to tell the story.

2. Your facilitator will share an appreciation story with you and ask for feedback.

3. When your facilitator has finished reviewing 4+ Appreciation Stories with you, get ready to share your collected appreciation stories with each other as 4+ Stories.

Notes

4. Complete the Belonging 4+ Shalom Story With Appreciation Worksheet, page 35.
   a. Use your collected appreciation moments list to guide you, page 34. You completed this list for homework.
   b. Use your 4+ Appreciation Stories Worksheet to guide you throughout the exercise.
5. Break into groups of 3 with people from your Round Table.
6. Follow your facilitator's instructions as the first volunteer in each small group begins telling her or his story.
   a. You will have 3 minutes to tell your story.
   b. When your story is complete, ask for feedback, and your small group members will have 2 minutes to encourage you for every element of the story that you were able to include.
   c. Your facilitator will let you know when it's time to start feedback, and when the next volunteer can begin telling a story.
7. When each person has told a story and received feedback, celebrate your appreciation!

Please start the Belonging DVD for this week's lesson.

Belonging Teaching Notes: Wired for relationship: Discovering my brain's relational circuits

What does "Belonging" look like?
• Belonging is the joy we create around us!

Belonging is training!

Living in a relational world with our relational circuits fully active!

Weekly Bible Story: Yuck For Lunch
• The Story of Peter and Cornelius (Acts 10)
• What does this story show us about Peter's maturity and his ability to create belonging for people he previously despised?

Learning to Create Healthy Belonging:
• Infant: Creates belonging indiscriminately.
• Child: Creates belonging with family and friends, especially the same gender.
• Adult: Creates belonging with partners and "My Herd."
• Parent: Creates belonging for children.
• Elder: Creates belonging for communities and the family-less.

What happens if we get stuck at any stage?
• Infant: Dismissive, distracted, disorganized or reactive attachment (doesn't try to have attachments).
• Child: Creates rejection around themselves.
• Adult: Sexualized belonging: No discrimination in belonging.
• Parent: Pass on non-secure attachment styles and/or sexualized bonds.
• Elder: Only take care of own biological family or run cults or other controlling institutions.

WHEN WE FEEL SHALOM AND APPRECIATION:
Our brain works the way God designed it! With shalom and appreciation, our relationships sustain us, and our relationships are bigger and more important to us than the problems we experience in relationships. Shalom and appreciation help tame our cravings, and we more deeply experience God's presence with us.

How can we grow and learn to live in a relational world with our relational circuits fully active?
- Our minds and brains are designed for a relational world where everything is in shalom.

Shalom
- Everything is in the right relationship,
- In the right place,
- At the right strength,
- And the right amount,
- For God and people.
- Synchronized!

When we feel shalom and appreciation, our brain works the way God designed it!
- Our relationships sustain us.
- Relationships are bigger than problems.
- Our cravings are tamed.
- We know that God is with us.

We are so full of life that we create belonging around us for:
- Plants.
- Animals.
- Nature.
- People.
- Spiritual Family.

At the center of this shalom (synchronization) are our brain's relational circuits.

Living in shalom and appreciation with our brain's relational circuits fully alive is how we thrive!
- This is where we want to live!

This is why:
- Growing our capacity for shalom and appreciation, and
- Learning to notice when we are living in shalom and appreciation – with our RCs fully active,
- Are essential goals in Belonging!

We want to reset our nervous system:
- We want to grow so much capacity for shalom and appreciation with our RCs fully active that they are what "normal" feels like to us.
- We want shalom, appreciation and active RCs to be our new emotional/relational "baseline."

When living in appreciation and God's Peace with active RCs feels "normal":
- It's easier to notice when our RCs are impaired, and that shalom and appreciation are missing.

We can more quickly realize that our emotional and relational capacity has dropped before we make a mess!

Capacity: How much can it hold before it breaks?

WE WANT TO COMPLETELY RESET OUR NERVOUS SYSTEM.

We want to grow so much capacity for shalom and appreciation with our RCs fully active that they are what "normal" feels like to us. We want shalom, appreciation and active RCs to be our new emotional/relational "baseline." Learning to live in shalom and appreciation with our RCs fully active is how we thrive!

Notes

Relational Capacity: How much emotional and relational intensity can you hold before your brain's relational circuits overload?

If we lose our shalom, especially in relationships:
• Our vital relational circuits that help us create and experience belonging can start to shut down.

When our relational circuits are off or partially shut down:
• Problems get bigger than our relationships.
• We can treat people like objects.
• Cravings become monsters.
• We can deeply hurt those we love the most.
• When we express feelings and opinions, they become deadly weapons.
• Communication hurts others instead of creating belonging and bringing shalom to the situation.
• This is not where we want to live!

When my brain and spirit are in shalom, I am:
• Open.
• Flexible.
• Interested.
• Self-reflective.

When my brain and spirit are in shalom, I can:
• Use all my senses.
• Work with you to reach understanding.
• Stay connected.

In shalom, when my relational circuits are working, I can:
• Receive.
• Process.
• Respond.
• Explore.
• Understand.
• Join.
• I Create Belonging!

Without shalom, our brain suspends the very best brain and relational functions.
• Self-reflection: Now I don't see my part and what is possible for me.
• Attunement: Now I don't feel like anyone connects with me.
• Mindsight: Now I don't feel like I have a friend in the world.

Trying to deal with people when our relational circuits are off is a lot like driving a car if we're drunk!

TRYING TO RELATE TO PEOPLE WITH OUR RELATIONAL CIRCUITS OFF IS A LOT LIKE TRYING TO DRIVE A CAR IF WE'RE DRUNK!

Wouldn't it be better to learn to monitor and restore our brain's RCs before we need relational air bags? That's why learning to use the Belonging RC Checklists to notice how well our RCs are working are important goals in Belonging.

- The resulting damage to our life and relationships can be very painful.
- Hurt…Tragedy…Regret…Relapse…Loss.
- All occur when our RCs are not working.

Wouldn't it be better to learn to monitor our relational circuits before we need the air bags?

Learning to use the Belonging Checklists for Relational Circuits can help you learn to recognize when your relational circuits are on:
- When you are alone, with friends or in an intimate relationship.

Learning to use the checklist to recognize how well our RCs are working is important.
- Learning to restore our RCs when we are distressed is also important.

When we learn to restore our RCs, we are better able to:
- Live in shalom and appreciation.
- Build increased capacity.
- Create belonging around ourselves.
- Grow stronger life-giving connections with God and others.
- Stay connected when we're upset – and make fewer relational messes!

The process of learning to restore our RCs and return to shalom and appreciation is called "Quieting" and is an essential element of Belonging.
- Because we can be distressed in body, soul and heart, we need to learn to bring quiet and shalom to distress we feel in each of these areas.

Today, we are going to work on noticing how well our RCs are working.

Next week, we'll learn how to:
- Quiet our distress, and bring shalom to our body, soul and heart.
- Jump-start our RCs.
- Return to God's Peace and appreciation.

It is always amazing how much better relationships work when our brain is running… and not just our mouth or emotions!
- Let's learn the checklist!

We'll cover the short form now. Your facilitator will help you with the long form in a few minutes.

Check your relational circuits!

MY BELONGING SHORT FORM RC CHECKLIST

- ❑ I just want to make a problem, person or feeling go away.
- ❑ I don't want to listen to what others feel or say.
- ❑ My mind is "locked onto" something upsetting.
- ❑ I don't want to be connected to? (someone I usually like)
- ❑ I just want to get away, or fight or I freeze.
- ❑ I more aggressively interrogate, judge and fix others.

Notes

Belonging Exercise: Check your Relational Circuits: Learning to use the Belonging Long Form RC Checklist

You will have 15 minutes for this exercise, as your facilitator teaches you to use the RC Long Form Checklist.

Exercise Instructions

1. Remain at your Round Table for this exercise.

2. Find your Belonging Long Form RC Checklist in Chapter 3 of your Belonging Workbook, pages 50-51.

3. As your facilitator guides you through the checklist, mark each statement that describes you right now.

4. You will have 15 minutes.

Belonging Homework: Week 3

Belonging Coordinators
- Send everyone in your Round Table an email with the list of the 3 ways that everyone at your table likes to receive belonging, page 47.
- Email this list to your facilitator and other Belonging Coordinators this week.

Everyone
- Use your RC Checklist to notice when your RCs are on – and off – this week.
- Pay attention to what it feels like when they are on – and when they are off.

Coordinators: 3 Ways Everyone at my Round Table Likes to Receive Belonging from Others

©Copyright E. James Wilder Ph.D. and Ed Khouri, 2009.

Instructions: This week, Round Table members will be asked to share their favorite ways of receiving the gift of belonging to others. They will give you 3 words to describe what they like to receive to feel that someone is "glad you are here." Write each of these words down.

This week, you will email your list to everyone in your Round Table and to other Belonging Coordinators.

Name	Receive Belonging 1	Receive Belonging 2	Receive Belonging 3

Notes

Relational Circuits Checklist And Worksheet

©Copyright E. James Wilder Ph.D. and Ed Khouri, 2009. Includes items from the Lehman Relational Connection Circuit Checklist by Karl Lehman M.D. Used by permission.

Overview

Our minds and brains are designed to live in a relational world where everything is in shalom. This Hebrew word means everything is in the right relationship, at the right time, in the right place, at the right strength and in the right amount for God and people. In the Life Model we call this being synchronized. When we are at shalom, our brain works well, our relationships sustain us, problems seem smaller, our cravings are tamed pets and God is in the air around us.

In shalom we build belonging around us for plants, animals, nature, people and spiritual family. At the center of this synchronization are our brain's relational circuits. If we lose our peace (particularly in relationships) these relational circuits can start to shut down. With our vital relational circuits partly or deeply off, problems get bigger, we can treat people like objects, our cravings become monsters, we can deeply hurt those we love, expressing feelings and opinions becomes a weapon, and communication hurts others instead of bringing shalom.

When the best of our brain and spirit are in shalom, we are open, interested, flexible, self-reflective and use all our senses. We work to have the other person collaborate with us to reach understanding. We receive, process, respond, explore, understand and join[1]. When we lose shalom, our brain suspends the best brain and relational functions:[2]

Self reflection	SUSPENDED	Now I don't see my part and what is possible for me.
Attunement	SUSPENDED	Now I don't feel like anyone connects with me.
Mindsight	SUSPENDED	Now I don't feel like I have a friend in the world.

Just like we should not drive when drunk or even "buzzed," we should not try to deal with people and our problems with our relational circuits "off." To avoid hurt, tragedy, regret, relapse and loss, here is a basic checklist to see if your relational circuits are on - whether you are alone or in an intimate relationship. Of course, the best part is that there are some specific steps you can take to start your relational circuits going once again. You will be amazed how much better you feel when your brain is running and not just your mouth or emotions. Here is how Dr. Lehman describes the goal as a part of the Immanuel lifestyle developed in Belonging and Thriving Recovery.

Lehman Relational Connection Circuit Restoration Steps:[3]

My goal is to perceive the Lord's presence, tell Him about my pain, and receive His Shalom so that I can get my relational connection circuits back on line. (My goal is not to fix the problem that is upsetting me or even resolve any underlying trauma.) EVERYTHING with respect to my relational conflicts will turn out better once my relational circuits are back on.

My strategy is to talk to God about my emotions and thoughts even if I don't perceive His presence since my relational circuits are off. (I do not talk to God about the person who I am upset with as that keeps my relational circuits off.) I invite the Lord to be with me in my pain, asking Him to help me perceive His presence.

---

1 Page 89 <u>Parenting From The Inside Out</u> by Daniel Siegel and Mary Hartzell.

2 Page 159 <u>Parenting From The Inside Out</u> by Daniel Siegel and Mary Hartzell.

3 Lehman Relational Connection Circuit Checklist, by Karl Lehman M.D. Used by permission. For further information, visit www.kclehman.com.

RC Restoration Steps in Belonging

In Belonging, we will use a more basic approach to restarting our relational connection circuits. It all starts with skillfully learning to use this checklist to recognize when our circuits are on and when they are off. Since it only takes a second for our relational circuits to go offline - and it may be hours before we even notice - the checklist will also help us learn to recognize the cravings, problems and urges that grow when our circuits are off. We'll even provide you with a short handy version of the relational circuits connection checklist to carry with you. Stop and check!

Belonging Steps to Restart My Relational Circuits When They Are OFF

1. Shalom for my body
   A. Physically reduce my fear and adrenalin immediately
   B. Physically activate my stress reduction system (parasympathetic)
   C. Physically enter a quiet place for my body and now my mind as well

2. Shalom for my Soul (Validation) by talking directly to God about my emotions and thoughts even though I don't perceive His presence. I do NOT talk to God about the other person I am upset with as that keeps my relational circuits OFF!

3. Shalom for my Heart (Comfort) by feeling sad about those things that grieve us both. This activates the ventromedial circuits and parasympathetic system in my brain.

4. Grow my appreciation and put it in my memory for future use through strong appreciation and storytelling.

We began practicing Step 4 in week 2. We will learn Shalom for my Body and Shalom for my Soul and Heart starting in week 4.

Important note: The inability to restore relational circuit functions is a sign that healing is needed. Healing will be addressed in the Healing module of Thriving Recovery and through the Immanuel Process. Some healing requires more ministry than Thriving Recovery alone provides.

Not everyone has the same experience with relational circuits. Some people will recognize that they rarely have these circuits on in their adult lives. Those who need to start waking up their relational circuits will need lots of practice on all of the steps. Those whose relational circuits are rarely off may only need a few. Use the steps you need, and if you are having a lot of difficulty, it is likely a sign of attachment pain that needs healing. We will be looking at this more in Healing and Loving. You may also need more focused ministry times outside this class for some blockages that are particularly resistant.

Notes

The Belonging Checklist For Relational Circuits

©Copyright by E. James Wilder Ph.D. and Ed Khouri 2009.

General signs that my relational circuits are OFF:

- ❏ I just want to make a problem, person or feeling stop and go away.
- ❏ My mind is "locked onto" something upsetting.
- ❏ I think, say, repeat a word, phrase, cliché or thought that is negative, insulting or profane.
- ❏ I feel like screaming, name-calling or threatening (or I do).[4]
- ❏ I strongly want to retaliate.
- ❏ I determine the only acceptable response that someone else can give me.
- ❏ I just want to get away or fight or I freeze.[5]
- ❏ I become aggressive in the way I interrogate, judge or fix others.[6]
    - ❏ Interrogate – I ask aggressive questions about my hunch or fear of what someone is thinking, doing or feeling while looking for a particular response.
    - ❏ Judge – I use my questions to expose the things I disapprove of so I can prove myself right and win.
    - ❏ Fix – I already know what I want them to do or say and I use my questions (talking with them) to get my way or reach my goal.
- ❏ I feel like it is their fault if they get hurt. (They asked for it. They should just get out of my way. They should have thought of that!)
- ❏ I don't feel like listening to what others are feeling, saying or going to say.
- ❏ When others are talking, I am already figuring out what to say before they even finish.
- ❏ I don't want to make eye contact.
- ❏ I would rather just handle problems myself.
- ❏ People are a bother and/or get in my way.

If my answers are YES, then my relational circuits are OFF.

Additional questions to see if my relational circuits are ON when I am alone:

- ❏ I see this moment as a new situation where I can learn something. (It does not feel like a bad place I have been before.)
- ❏ I can reflect on myself (not just my hurts).
- ❏ I think of others who would understand me well if they were here now. (I am not struggling with feeling isolated and alone.)
- ❏ I am eager to talk with God about this situation.
- ❏ I want to encourage others to be helpful.

If I cannot check YES, then my relational connection circuits are OFF or weak.

---

4 Page 193 <u>Parenting From The Inside Out</u> by Daniel Siegel and Mary Hartzell.

5 Page 168 <u>Parenting From The Inside Out</u> by Daniel Siegel and Mary Hartzell.

6 Page 89 <u>Parenting From The Inside Out</u> by Daniel Siegel and Mary Hartzell.

Additional questions to see if my relational circuits are ON with people I do not know (well):

- ❏ I can be respectful.
- ❏ I am aware and interested in their point of view.
- ❏ I am open to understanding what they are feeling right now.
- ❏ I am aware of my own feelings and responses without having to blurt them out.
- ❏ I can join in give-and-take both verbally and nonverbally.
- ❏ I can help them make their points more clearly understandable. They will agree with my description because it does not make them look stupid.
- ❏ I can understand and accept it if they make a choice I do not like.

If I cannot check YES, then my relational connection circuits are OFF or weak.

Additional questions to see if my relational circuits are ON with people I know well:

- ❏ Can I remember why I wanted to be in relationship with them in the first place?
- ❏ Do my good memories of them seem important right now?
- ❏ Do I feel connected to _____ (someone I know well and usually like)?
- ❏ Do I feel a desire to be connected to _____ (someone I know well and usually like)?
- ❏ Do I experience him/her as a relational being?
- ❏ Am I aware of his/her care for me?
- ❏ Do I feel compassion about what he/she's thinking and feeling?
- ❏ Am I open to share their distressing feelings with them to help them return to joy?
- ❏ Do I perceive the presence of _____ (someone I know well and usually like) as a resource?
- ❏ Am I experiencing joy in being with him/her?

If I cannot check YES, then my relational connection circuits are OFF or weak.

EVERYTHING with respect to my relational conflicts, urges and cravings will turn out better once my relational circuits are back on.

Notes

Chapter 3: Questions for Further Discussion

1. Imagine that you were present in the story of Peter and Cornelius. Which of the following characters in this story do you most closely identify with? Why?
   a. Peter.
   b. Cornelius.
   c. Peter's friends.

2. In this week's lesson, we discussed how people at each stage of maturity create belonging, and what happens to our ability to create belonging if we become stuck at any stage. From this discussion, list your own stage of maturity, and how this affects your ability to create belonging.

3. What do you think your life would be like if your nervous system was reset so that appreciation and shalom were your normal experience? How would this change your relationship with God and with people who are important to you - and your ability to create belonging? To answer this question, please make a list including God and at least 5 other people. Describe how your relationship and ability to create belonging with each would change.

4. What does capacity mean to you? On an average day, how long does it take you to hit overwhelm? How can you tell that you've hit overwhelm?

5. What happens in your relationships when you lose shalom and appreciation, and your RCs start to fade? Use the list of relationships you made in question #3, and describe what happens in each when your RCs fade, and you've lost shalom and appreciation.

6. What happens when you are able to see your relationships as bigger than problems? What happens when you make problems bigger than relationships?

7. How are your relationships different when your RCs are working?

8. This week, use the RC checklist daily to monitor your RCs. Make a list of the situations each day in which you knew your RCs were working, and make a list of the situations that caused your RCs to fade.

9. We want to become skilled at noticing when our RCs are working, and when they are not. After using the short and long RC checklists, what are the best indicators that your RCs are working or not working?

Notes

Notes

54

Notes

Belonging Chapter 4:

QUIETING TO RESTORE BELONGING:
SHALOM FOR MY BODY,
SHALOM FOR MY SOUL AND HEART.

Group Opens:
• Ask a volunteer to open the group with prayer.

Belonging exercise: Creating belonging for another Round Table
As a Round Table, pick a way to express belonging and "We want you to come back" to another Round Table next week. You will have 10 minutes, and your facilitator will keep track of time for you.

1. Remain at your Round Table for this exercise.

2. Table 1 will choose a way to express belonging and "we want you to come back" to Table 2, Table 2 will do this for Table 3, etc. The last table will do this for Table 1. Use the Round Table numbers your facilitator assigned in week 1 to identify your target table.

3. Your Coordinator will:
   a. Check and find out how many people are in your target table.
   b. Help you pick one item from a list of suggestions, and you can leave your gifts on a chair for your target table when you arrive for class next week.

4. Remember: Be sure to leave your gift for your target table when you arrive for group because there will be no time in class to give something personally.

5. Use your personal belonging styles as you decide how to create belonging!

6. Coordinators: Complete the "Expressing Belonging to Another RT project" worksheet on page 63 to record your Table's plan.

7. Here are some Round Table ideas for creating belonging:
   a. A blessing card you made
   b. A snack you like to share or some bottled water
   c. A flower
   d. A coupon they can redeem from you for any of the following:
      I.   Something you will pray for them about next week
      II. A one minute neck rub
      III. Anything free or less than $1 that makes them feel special
      IV. A fresh fruit of their choice next week.
      V.   Something you think about or create on your own!

Belonging exercise: Round Table Discussion.
You will have 15 minutes for this exercise, and your facilitator will keep track of time for you.

1. Remain at your Round Table for this exercise.

2. Please share and discuss your answers to these questions with your group:
   a. How did you do with your RC Checklists this week?
   b. What did you notice about when your RCs were on – and when they were off?
   c. When did you use the checklist, and which one did you use?

Please start the Belonging DVD for this week's lesson.

Notes

Belonging Teaching: Quieting to restore belonging: Shalom for my Body, Shalom for my Soul and Heart

What does "Belonging" look like?
• Belonging is the joy we create around us!

Belonging is training!

Weekly Bible Study: The story of David and Saul
• Staying relational and learning to quiet distress.
• Making relationships bigger than problems.

Quieting:
• Shalom for my Body.
• Shalom for my Soul and Heart.

Appreciation, Shalom & RCs: A quick review.

Our minds and brains are designed for a relational world where everything is in shalom.

Shalom
• Everything is in the right relationship,
• In the right place,
• At the right strength,
• And the right amount,
• For God and people.
• Synchronized!

With God's Peace and appreciation, our brain's RCs (relational circuits) allow us to connect inter-actively with God and others.

Living in shalom and appreciation with our brain's relational circuits fully alive is how we thrive!
• This is where we want to live!

Let's try a simple exercise.
• What does it feel like when you feel "connected" to God and others?
• How does this list compare to your answers on the "What does appreciation feel like to me?" Worksheet in Week 2 on page 31.
    o Do they feel the same?
• Have you experienced shalom?
    o What does it feel like to you?
    o How does this compare with connection and appreciation?
    o Can you really experience shalom and appreciation without connections to God and others?
• Isn't this where you really want to live?

Pause the DVD for a 5 minute class exercise.

> ### BELONGING QUESTIONS:
> *What does it feel like when you feel connected to God and others?*
> *Does it feel a lot like shalom and appreciation?*
> *Can you experience deep shalom and appreciation without relationship?*

Belonging Exercise: What does it feel like when you feel connected to God and others?

Your facilitator will lead this short 7 minute class discussion exercise.

1. Remain at your Round Table for this exercise as your facilitator leads a short class discussion to answer the questions from the video. You will find these questions on your "What Does it Feel Like when You Feel Connected to God and Others?" Worksheet located in chapter 4 of your workbook, page 62.

2. As your facilitator leads you through this exercise, please share one-word answers to each question with the class.

3. Write any answers that apply to you in the space provided on the worksheet.

4. You will have 7 minutes, and when you are finished, please restart the DVD.

Please restart the DVD.

Learning to live in appreciation and shalom with my RCs fully active is an essential Belonging skill because then:
- Our relationships sustain us.
- Relationships are bigger than problems.
- Our cravings are tamed.
- We know that God is with us.

We are so full of life that we create belonging around us for:
- Plants.
- Animals.
- Nature.
- People.
- Spiritual Family.

My emotional and relational capacity grows.

Relational Capacity:
- How much emotional and relational intensity can you hold before your brain's relational circuits overload?

At the center of this shalom (synchronization) are our brain's relational circuits.

We want to hit our relational and emotional reset button.
- We want to grow so much capacity for shalom and appreciation with our RCs fully active that this becomes our new, "normal" emotional and relational experience.

If we lose our shalom and appreciation, especially in relationships,
- Then our vital relational circuits that help us create and experience Belonging start to shut down.

> ### RELATIONAL CAPACITY:
> *How much emotional and relational intensity can you hold before you feel overwhelmed and your brain's relational circuits overload? The greater our capacity, the longer we can stay connected with God and others when we are distressed or upset.*

Notes

Trying to deal with people when our relational circuits are off is a lot like trying to drive a car if we're drunk!

Blasting Others
- When our mouth and emotions are more engaged than our brain, we overwhelm others and cause their relational circuits to shut down.

It is always amazing how much better relationships work when our brain is running... and not just our mouth or emotions!
- Let's stop for a quick RC Check using the Belonging RC Short Form.

Check your relational circuits!
- ❑ I just want to make a problem, person or feeling go away.
- ❑ I don't want to listen to what others feel or say.
- ❑ My mind is "locked onto" something upsetting.
- ❑ I don't want to be connected to? (someone I usually like)
- ❑ I just want to get away, or fight or I freeze.
- ❑ I more aggressively interrogate, judge and fix others.

Now that we're learning to notice shalom, appreciation and RCs:
- How can we grow our ability to return to God's Peace and appreciation?
- How can we restore our RCs when they are impaired?
- How can we learn to quiet the distress our body, soul and heart feel when we are upset?
- How can we bring shalom to our body, soul and heart so that we can return to God's Peace and appreciation with our RCs active?

Belonging Quieting Steps:
- Shalom for My Body.
- Shalom for My Soul (Validation).
- Shalom for My Heart (Comfort).
- Grow my appreciation.

Important note: Not everyone has the same experience with relational circuits. Use the steps you need.
- If you have never really had your RCs on, you will need lots of practice on the first few steps.
- If your RCs are rarely off, you may need only the last few.

If you have lots of difficulty with RCs:
- It is often a sign of attachment pain that needs to be healed.
- We'll talk about attachment pain later in Belonging, and in the Healing and Loving Modules.
- You may also need more focused ministry time outside of class for difficult blockages.

So what is quieting? And how do I learn to bring shalom to my body, soul and heart?

Quieting means calming my body, soul and heart when I am upset so that I can:

QUIETING MEANS:

Calming the distress in my body, soul and heart so that I can return to shalom and appreciation with my RCs active - so that I can reconnect with God and with others. Shalom for my Body and Shalom for my Soul and Heart help me learn to quiet myself.

- Return to shalom and appreciation with my RCs active,
- Re-connect with God and others,
- Create belonging.

Quieting my Body:
- The Shalom for my Body exercise can help calm my body when I am feeling angry or fearful and anxious.

Angry and fearful reactions do not activate our brain's relational quieting circuits in the ventromedial prefrontal cortex.
- Anger and fear tend to make relational problems worse!

Shalom for my Body: Helps activate my body's stress reduction systems and quieting circuitry to help calm my body's fear, anxiety and anger responses.
- Right now, we are going to learn the Shalom for my Body short form exercise, and then you'll stop the DVD to practice.
- There is a also a longer series of Shalom for my Body exercises located in the appendix of your workbook for you to try at home.

Let's try Shalom for my Body.
- The instructions are on the back of your RC Card.

Shalom My Body Short Form
    a. Set the timing right with the verse based on Psalm 56:3: "Whenever I am afraid I will trust in you O Lord."
    b. Move your body (4 moves).
    c. Breathe and scrunch
    d. Yawn left and right
    e. Knock to wake up your attachment center
    f. Get the sympathetic and parasympathetic synchronized with each other (change speeds).

Pause the DVD for a class exercise.

Belonging Exercise: Shalom for my Body
In this exercise, everyone has the opportunity to learn and practice the Shalom for my Body exercise you just saw demonstrated on the Belonging video. Your facilitator will lead the entire class through the exercise. You will have 7 minutes.

1. It's your turn to try the Shalom for my Body Exercise.

2. Remain at your Round Table, and make sure you have enough space around you to lean back with your arms spread out wide.

3. Follow your facilitator's instructions as he or she leads you through Shalom for my Body practice.

4. You will have 5 minutes for this exercise, and when you are finished, please turn the DVD back on.

SHALOM FOR MY BODY

Helps activate my body's stress reduction systems and my brain's quieting circuitry to help quiet my body's fear, anxiety or anger responses. By helping quiet my body, I can then begin to talk with God about my distressing situation and relationships.

Notes

Please restart the DVD.

Learning to quiet distress in my Soul and Heart.
• Shalom for my Soul and Heart

When upsetting negative emotions exceed my emotional and relational capacity, my soul is distressed.
• My RCs start to shut down, and I lose my shalom and appreciation.
• Because my RCs shut down, I feel very much alone in my pain.

When I lose shalom and appreciation – and my RCs shut down, I also lose Godsight.
• Now, I am more distressed, because I can't see what God sees in my situation.
• I can't see myself, others or my situation like He does.

To return to God's Peace and appreciation with my RCs active, I need shalom for my heart and soul.

The process of quieting my soul and heart is called Affirmation.

Affirmation has 2 parts:
• Shalom for my Soul: Validation
• Shalom for my Heart: Comfort.

Shalom for my Soul: Validation
• God affirms our relationship and the importance of my distressing feelings as I share what I am experiencing or have experienced with Him.
• I honestly share my upsetting situation, thoughts and feelings with God, and invite Him to be with me, and remind me of His presence.
• I connect with God right in the middle of my distress, and discover that I am loved and accepted, even when I am upset.
• God quiets us with His loving presence, and affirms the value of our relationship and the importance of our feelings.
• Validation comes before comfort.

Shalom for my Heart: Comfort
• Discovering God's perspective and viewpoint about what I am experiencing now or have experienced in the past.
• Comfort helps me see what God sees in me, my situation and others involved in my situation.
• God's sight is always relational, so comfort includes the truth about my situation – and His heart towards me and everyone involved.
• God's sight always helps me recognize the difference between the way God sees things – and my pain-clouded, distorted perceptions of God, myself, others and my distressing situation.
• Comfort helps me separate my distressing emotions and thoughts from the way things really are.
• Comfort always comes after validation.

SHALOM FOR MY SOUL AND HEART:
The process of quieting my soul and heart is called affirmation.
Validation brings shalom to my soul and quiets my distressing thoughts and emotions.
Comfort restores Godsight so I can see myself, others and my situation like God does.

Together, validation and comfort bring shalom to our Soul and Heart.
- We can return to appreciation and God's Peace with our RCs fully active.

Let's try the Shalom for my Soul and Heart Worksheet.
- Locate your worksheet, and get ready for shalom practice!
- When you are finished, check your RCs again.

Belonging exercise: Shalom for my Soul and Heart with an RC Check
You will have 20 minutes for the Shalom for my Soul and Heart Exercise, and the RC Check.

Instructions: Shalom for my Soul and Heart

1. Remain at your Round Table for this exercise.

2. You will need your Shalom for my Soul and Heart guidelines for this exercise. The Shalom for my Soul and Heart form is located on page 64 of your workbook.

3. Follow your facilitator's instructions as he or she leads you through the worksheet.

4. Your facilitator will explain each section of the worksheet to you, and help you complete it in class.

5. When you have finished, check your relational circuits using the RC Card.

Instructions:

1. Remain at your Round Table, as your facilitator leads you through a short form RC Check.

2. Belonging Short Form RC Checklist:
   - ❑ I just want to make a problem, person or feeling go away.
   - ❑ I don't want to listen to what others feel or say.
   - ❑ My mind is "locked onto" something upsetting.
   - ❑ I don't want to be connected to? (someone I usually like)
   - ❑ I just want to get away, or fight or I freeze.
   - ❑ I more aggressively interrogate, judge and fix others.

Belonging Homework: Week 4

Belonging Coordinators
- Send everyone in your Round Table an email reminding them of the project to create belonging for another Round Table. Thank everyone for participating!

Everyone
- Prepare your expression of belonging for your target Round Table using as much of your own style as will fit with the project. Bring your gift to class.
- Practice using your RC Checklist.
- Try your Shalom exercises to restore appreciation, God's Peace and your RCs as needed.

> ### BOTH VALIDATION AND COMFORT ARE NEEDED.
> *In validation, God lets me know that He values our relationship and my feelings.*
> *In comfort, God shares His viewpoint about the situation with me.*
> *Validation always comes before comfort.*

Notes

What Does it Feel Like When You Feel "Connected" to God and Others?

©Copyright E. James Wilder Ph.D. and Ed Khouri, 2009.

Use this worksheet to make a list of the words suggested by the class as we share answers to this question. Be sure to highlight any words that describe how you feel.

When I feel "connected" with God and others, I feel:

How does this list compare to the list on the "What does appreciation feel like to me?" Worksheet page 31? Are the feelings similar?

Can you really experience deep shalom and appreciation without being relationally connected to God and others?

Notes

Coordinators: Expressing Belonging to Another Round Table Project

©Copyright E. James Wilder Ph.D. and Ed Khouri, 2009.

Instructions:

In this week's project, you will help your Round Table choose a way to express belonging and "We want you to come back" to another Round Table. Use this form to record the number of people at your target Round Table and the expression of belonging that your Round Table chooses to give. You will need one expression of belonging for each person in the target table.

Please remind members to prepare their expression of belonging to the target table with as much of their own personal style as will fit with the idea your Round Table chooses. Your table should pick one from the ideas shown in class or you can choose your own.

This week, send an email to your Round Table members reminding them of the project – and express appreciation to them for participating!

Which Round Table is our belonging target?

How many people are in the target Round Table?

Group Suggestions:

Our Round Table will create belonging by:

Quieting: Shalom for my Soul and Heart
©Copyright E. James Wilder Ph.D. and Ed Khouri, 2009.

Our goal: Quiet the distress our soul and heart feel so that we can return to shalom and appreciation with our relational circuits restored.

Instructions: Honestly share your answers to each question, with all the feeling you can express, out loud with God. If you feel angry, answer the questions on the "Anger" side of your worksheet. If you feel anxious or fearful, answer the questions on the Anxious/Fearful side of the worksheet. If you are feeling very distressed, angry or anxious/fearful, it is a good idea to practice your Shalom for my Body worksheet first. When you have finished, see if you can remember any promises God has made you.

If I am feeling Angry:	If I am feeling Anxious or Fearful
1. What happened that has upset me?	1. What happened that has upset me?
2. What feels so unfair about this situation?	2. What feels threatening about this situation?
Keep telling God what feels unfair about your situation until you are also able to tell God how your body feels right now.	*Keep telling God what feels threatening about your situation until you are also able to tell God how your body feels right now.*
After 5 minutes, if you still feel very angry, focus on any part of your situation that is sad. Tell God how you and others have been hurt in this situation, and how your body feels now. Is there any part of this situation that makes God sad?	*After 5 minutes, if you still feel very anxious or scared, focus on any part of your situation that is sad. Tell God how you and others have been hurt in this situation, and how your body feels now. Is there any part of this situation that makes God sad?*
3. Ask God to show you where He sees you were hurt most. *(Sometimes this is a repeating injury and brings up other hurts.)*	3. Ask God to give you shelter.
4. What is different about this situation now that God and I are looking at things together?	4. What is different about this situation now that God and I are looking at things together?
5. What do I appreciate or long for when God joins me? Share your appreciation with God and tell Him what your longing feels like.	5. What do I appreciate or long for when God joins me? Share your appreciation with God and tell Him what your longing feels like.

Chapter 4: Questions for Further Discussion

1. What is it like for you when you feel "connected" with God and with others? What emotions do you feel, and what does your body feel like? Is this similar or different from how appreciation and shalom feel to you? Do you think it is possible to feel shalom and appreciation without connections with God and others?

2. How do you feel when your RCs are starting to shut down? What happens to your emotions and what does your body feel? What happens to your relationships, cravings and ability to create belonging? Be as specific as you can.

3. Have you ever "blasted" someone when your RCs were off? What happened to you, to the other person and to belonging? Have you ever been "blasted" by another person when their RCs were off? What happened to you, to the other person and belonging? What do these suggest about the importance of our RCs?

4. What is quieting, and why is it an important skill? What does quieting help us do?

5. What happened when you tried the Shalom for my Body exercise in class? How did you feel before and after - and what happened to your RCs?

6. What is affirmation, and how does it help us quiet? What are the 2 important parts of affirmation that help us quiet?

7. Describe "Validation" and how it helps bring shalom to our soul. Have you ever experienced validation and the affirmation of your relationship and the importance of your feelings when you were distressed? How did it feel, and how did it bring shalom to your soul? What was different, and how did it affect your RCs and ability to create belonging?

8. Describe "Comfort" and how it helps bring shalom to our heart. Have you ever experienced comfort and the restoration of Godsight? How did it feel, and how did it bring shalom to your heart? What was different, and how did it affect your RCs and ability to create belonging?

9. What happened when you tried the Shalom for my Soul and Heart exercise? How did you feel before and after - and what happened to your RCs?

Notes

Belonging Chapter 5:

QUIETING, AFFIRMATION AND BELONGING:
WHY DO PEOPLE LIKE YOU ANYWAY?

Group Opens:
• Ask a volunteer to open the group with prayer.

Belonging exercise: Discussion Questions
This is a 5 minute exercise, and your facilitator will keep track of time for you.

1. Form groups of 3 from your Round Table.

2. Share your answers to the following question: In one word, how does it feel when you create belonging around you "your own favorite way?"

3. You will have 5 minutes, and your facilitator will keep track of time for you.

Please start the Belonging DVD for this week's lesson.

Week 5 Teaching Notes: Quieting, Affirmation, and Belonging

What does "Belonging" look like?
• Belonging is the joy we create around us!

Belonging is training!

Check your relational circuits!
- ❑ I just want to make a problem, person or feeling go away.
- ❑ I don't want to listen to what others feel or say.
- ❑ My mind is "locked onto" something upsetting.
- ❑ I don't want to be connected to? (someone I usually like)
- ❑ I just want to get away, or fight or I freeze.
- ❑ I more aggressively interrogate, judge and fix others.

Why Do People Like You?
• People like others who take large, negative feelings and make them smaller!

When things are going badly, if someone is able to make the feelings not quite as big and intense:
• You will have the strong feeling that you like her or him!

People like those who amplify joy.
• But they also actively shun those who amplify distress.

People may like being around you if you are able to amplify joy:
• As long as you don't overload everyone's circuits and allow them time to quiet and rest.

But if you also amplify distress, you will be actively:
• Rejected.
• Left alone in your pain.

Notes

- The object of retaliation and rebellion.
- Shunned & ditched.
- Cut off & cut out.
- Punished & disrespected.
- Tuned out & ignored.

If my brain's ventromedial circuits are off, I will amplify distress. This may be true if:
- I have PTSD.
- I am in attachment pain.
- I am running Memorex.
- I am hormonal.
- I am borderline with a family history of two generations of abuse.
- I am fearful or running on adrenaline.

People who are craving and in attachment pain are likely to amplify distress:
- If there is even a hint of something negative going on, they will amplify it.
- They won't appreciate or build on positive things.

It won't be long until people avoid me, shun me, punish me, ignore me or just tune me out.
- All because I make problems bigger than relationships!
- Wouldn't it be better to avoid the relational crash – and learn to quiet when we're upset?

Learning to keep my relational circuits on and learning to live in shalom and appreciation help make my relationships bigger than my problems.

I must also learn to quiet – not amplify – the distress my body, soul and heart feel when I am upset.

Quieting is the process of calming the distress we experience in our body, soul and heart so that we can return to shalom and appreciation with our RCs fully active.

Learning to quiet my emotional/relational distress helps keep my relationships bigger than my problems.
- Quieting also creates belonging around me.

Weekly Bible Story: When problems get bigger than relationships: Cain, Abel, distress and belonging

If we lose our shalom and appreciation, especially in relationships, then our vital relational circuits that help us create and experience Belonging start to shut down.

I can only make relationships bigger than my problems when appreciation, shalom and RCs are restored.

Prepare to pause the DVD for a 10 minute Round Table exercise to answer the following questions:
- Have you ever seen people make problems bigger than relationships?
- Have you ever seen someone make relationships bigger than problems?

WHY DO PEOPLE LIKE YOU?

People like others who take large, negative feelings and make them smaller! When things are going badly, if someone is able to keep relationships bigger than the problems and make the distressing feelings not quite as big and intense, then you will have the strong feeling that you like them!

Part 1: 3 Minutes
- In your Round Table, you will have 3 minutes to share examples you have seen of people who made problems seem bigger and relationships smaller.

Part 2: 7 Minutes
- Now, take 7 minutes to share stories of people making relationships bigger than problems (especially if you have ever seen a person with an adult, parent or elder level of maturity handle a situation like this) and how their RCs either stayed on or reactivated.

Pause the DVD for a Belonging Exercise.

Belonging Exercise: Relationships Bigger Than Problems
Pause the DVD for this 10 minute Round Table exercise.

1. Remain at your Round Table for this exercise. Your facilitator will keep track of time for you.

2. Share your answers to the questions in parts 1 and 2.

3. Part 1: 3 Minutes
   a. Have you ever seen people make problems bigger than relationships?
   b. Share examples of people you have seen who made problems seem bigger and relationships smaller.

4. Part 2: 7 Minutes
   a. Have you ever seen someone make relationships bigger than problems?
   b. Share stories of people making relationships bigger than problems (especially if you have ever seen a person with an adult, parent or elder level of maturity handle a situation like this) and how this person's RCs either stayed on or reactivated.

5. When you are finished, restart the DVD.

Please restart the DVD.

Belonging Quieting Steps:
- Shalom for My Body.
- Shalom for My Soul (Validation).
- Shalom for My Heart (Comfort).
- Grow my appreciation.

Important note: Not everyone has the same experience with relational circuits.

Use the steps you need.
- If you have never really had your RCs on, you will need lots of practice on the first few steps.
- If your RCs are rarely off, you may need only the last few.

If you have lots of difficulty with RCs, it is often a sign of attachment pain that needs to be healed.
- We'll talk about attachment pain later in Belonging, and in the Healing and Loving Modules.
- You may also need more focused ministry time outside of class for difficult blockages.

WHY DON'T PEOPLE LIKE YOU?
People tend to actively reject, shun, avoid, disrespect, punish, ignore, retaliate and rebel against people who makes problems bigger than relationships by consistently amplifying upsetting feelings when they are distressed. Learning to quiet our distress helps us create belonging - and not rejection - around ourselves.

Notes

Shalom for my Body

- The Shalom for my Body Exercise calms and quiets my body when I am feeling fearful, anxious or angry.

Angry and fearful reactions do not activate our brain's relational quieting circuits in the ventromedial prefrontal cortex.
- Anger and fear tend to make relational problems worse!

Shalom for my Body
- Helps activate my body's stress reduction systems and quieting circuitry to help calm my body's fear, anxiety and anger responses.
- We learned this exercise last week.

Shalom My Body: Short Form
- Set the timing right with the verse: "Whenever I am afraid I will trust in you O Lord."
- Move your body (4 moves).
- Breathe and scrunch.
- Yawn left and right.
- Knock to wake up your attachment center.
- Get the sympathetic and parasympathetic synchronized with each other (change speeds).

Shalom for my Soul and Heart.

When upsetting negative emotions exceed my emotional and relational capacity, my soul is distressed.
- My RCs start to shut down, and I lose my shalom and appreciation.
- Because my RCs shut down, I feel very much alone in my pain.

When I lose shalom and appreciation and my RCs shut down, I also lose Godsight.
- Now, I am more distressed, because I can't see what God sees in my situation.
- I can't see myself, others or my situation like He does.

To return to God's Peace and appreciation with my RCs active, I need shalom for my heart and soul.

The process of quieting my soul & heart is called Affirmation.

Affirmation has 2 parts:
- Shalom for my Soul: Validation.
- Shalom for my Heart: Comfort.

Shalom for my Soul: Validation

- God affirms our relationship and the importance of my distressing feelings as I share what I am experiencing or have experienced with Him.
- I honestly share my upsetting situation, thoughts and feelings with God, and invite Him to be with me, and remind me of His presence.
- This helps me connect with God right in the middle of my distress, and discover that I am loved and accepted, even when I am upset.

> ### VALIDATION:
> *As I honestly share my upsetting situation, thoughts and feelings with God, and invite Him to be with me and remind me of His presence, God quiets me with His loving presence. He affirms the value of our relationship together, and the importance of my distressing feelings to Him.*

- God quiets us with His loving presence, and affirms the value of our relationship and the importance of our feelings.
- Validation comes before comfort.

Shalom for my Heart: Comfort
- Discovering God's perspective and viewpoint about what I am experiencing now or have experienced in the past.
- Comfort helps me see what God sees in me, my situation and others involved in my situation.
- God's sight is always relational, so comfort includes the truth about my situation – and His heart towards me and everyone involved.
- God's sight always helps me recognize the difference between the way God sees things – and my pain-clouded, distorted perceptions of God, myself, others and my distressing situation.
- Comfort helps me separate my distressing emotions and thoughts from the way things really are.
- Comfort always comes after validation.

Together, validation and comfort bring shalom to our soul and heart.
- We can return to appreciation and God's Peace with our RCs fully active.

Can we learn to recognize validation and comfort?

Remember:
- Validation: Sharing my distressing emotions with God as He affirms the value of our relationship and the importance of my feelings.
- Comfort: Discovering God's perspective and viewpoint about what I am experiencing.

Example: A child with a splinter: What could a parent say and do to bring validation and comfort to help a child quiet in this situation?
- Validation:
  o Oh! I am so sorry that you fell and got that splinter in your knee.
  o I can see how much it hurts you.
  o Come here and sit in my lap and let me hold you for awhile.
- Comfort:
  o I feel sad when you hurt because I don't like it when you are in pain.
  o Let's work together on getting that splinter out – and then your knee will stop hurting so much.
  o And after that, I'll fix the deck so you can play.

Example: The disciples and Jesus: What did Jesus say to help His disciples prepare for the rejection and persecution He knew was coming?
- Validation
  o Men will hate you and throw you out of the places where you have gathered with them – all because of me.
  o Because they hate me, they will hate you too – but I have chosen you and am always with you.

> ### COMFORT:
> *Comfort helps me see what God sees in me, my situation and others who are involved, so I can discover God's perspective about what I am experiencing now or have experienced in the past. God's sight is always relational, so comfort includes the truth about my situation -and His heart towards me and everyone involved.*

Notes

- Comfort
  - o I will never leave you or forsake you – and my shalom is not like anything you will ever experience here because it will never leave you.
  - o Know that when you are being persecuted, I am with you, and my Father will speak on your behalf!

Example: Domestic Abuse: What could validation and comfort sound like?
- Validation
  - o My dear one, I am so sorry that he hurt you like that.
  - o I want to hear all about it, and want to wipe away all of your tears.
  - o I know the deepest part of that hurt and how it has damaged your ability to love.
- Comfort
  - o I never wanted that to happen to you, and I wept with you when it happened.
  - o I want to restore everything you lost back to you – and even more!
  - o How can we keep you safe now so this doesn't happen again?

Learning to receive and recognize validation and comfort are essential – if we are going to successfully quiet distress in our soul and heart.
- But, this isn't the only reason that affirmation is important.

The lack of affirmation and quieting skills is very damaging to us.
- Without validation: Denial grows and flourishes.
- Without comfort: Fear grows and intensifies.

When denial and fear persist:
- Distress and emotional intensity increase.
- Self-quieting skills are not learned.
- Our relational identity becomes increasingly unstable.

But, affirmation received through validation and comfort help us quiet and change:
- How I see myself, God and others,
- My thoughts,
- The kinds of things I say to myself,
- My behavior,
- And help me develop a identity that is strong, relational and secure.

Let's get ready for shalom practice!
- Your facilitator will guide you through the Shalom for my Body, Soul and Heart exercises.
- Remember to check your RCs first!
- This time, see if you can spot the validation and comfort that bring shalom to your soul and heart.

But wait...there's even more! Let's Go Shalom Watching!

Go Shalom Watching:
- This tool, pages 76-77, will help you learn to track your experience with appreciation, shalom, RCs and quieting during the week. It will also help you look for validation and comfort as you quiet.

THE LACK OF AFFIRMATION IS VERY DAMAGING TO US:
Without validation, denial always grows and flourishes.
Without comfort, fear grows and intensifies.

- Your facilitator will teach you how to use this tool in class, and then for homework, you'll complete it and report your progress to your Round Table next week.
- Go Shalom Watching is a regular Belonging homework assignment.

Belonging exercise: RC Check
You will have 2 minutes for a quick RC Check using your short form.

Check your relational circuits!
- ❑ I just want to make a problem, person or feeling go away.
- ❑ I don't want to listen to what others feel or say.
- ❑ My mind is "locked onto" something upsetting.
- ❑ I don't want to be connected to? (someone I usually like)
- ❑ I just want to get away, or fight or I freeze.
- ❑ I more aggressively interrogate, judge and fix others.

Belonging Exercise: The Shalom Sequence: Shalom for my Body and Shalom for my Soul and Heart
You will have 20 minutes to complete the entire Shalom Sequence, and your facilitator will keep track of time for you. The Shalom for my Body exercise is 5 minutes, and Shalom for my Soul and Heart is 15 minutes.

Part 1: Shalom for my Body (5 Minutes)

1. Remain at your Round Table for this exercise.

2. Follow your facilitator's instructions as she or he leads the entire class in the Shalom for my Body exercise.
   a. Set the timing right with the verse based on Psalm 56:3: "Whenever I am afraid I will trust in you O Lord."
   b. Move your body (4 moves).
   c. Breathe and scrunch.
   d. Yawn left and right.
   e. Knock to wake up your attachment center.
   f. Get the sympathetic and parasympathetic synchronized with each other (change speeds).

Part 2: Shalom for my Soul and Heart (15 Minutes)

1. Remain at your Round Table for this exercise.

2. You will need your Shalom for my Soul and Heart guidelines for this exercise. The Shalom for my Soul and Heart form is located in Chapter 5 of your workbook, page 75.

3. Complete your worksheet on your own.
   a. If you are feeling angry, complete the sequence on the left column.
   b. If you are feeling fearful or anxious, complete the sequence on the right column.

4. Next, follow your facilitator's instructions so that you can share your worksheet out loud with God. Your facilitator may:
   a. Ask everyone to remain at their Round Table and share their worksheet with God out loud together.
   b. Designate specific areas around the room where you can go and share your worksheet with God.

5. As you share, please express yourself to God with as much feeling as you need to describe your situation.

6. When you have finished, or when time is up, please return to your Round Table.

Notes

Shalom Watching Instructions: Go Shalom Watching Worksheet
Your facilitator will have 10 minutes to teach you to use the Go Shalom Watching Worksheet.

1. Please remain at your Round Table as your facilitator explains how to complete your Go Shalom Watching Worksheet, pages 76-77.
   a. Use your Shalom Watching Worksheet every day to keep track of shalom, appreciation and your RCs.
   b. This worksheet is part of your homework assignment this week.
2. Follow your facilitator's instructions to learn how to use the worksheet for this week's homework assignment.
3. To complete your worksheet assignment this week:
   a. Briefly describe when you noticed that shalom, appreciation and your RCs were fading, and how the problem began.
   b. Place a check next to every statement that describes what happened when you lost shalom, appreciation and your RCs, and then place a check next to each step you used to restore them.
      I. If you lost shalom, appreciation and RCs this week, and it caused you to stop creating belonging, place a check next to the statement: "I stopped creating Belonging."
      II. This week, you do not need to pay attention to the statements about attachment pain, Godsight and cravings.
   c. Fill in the blanks to describe the validation and comfort you experienced.
   d. Finally, write one word that best describes what it felt like emotionally and in your body when you lost shalom, appreciation and your RCs – and when they were restored.

Belonging exercise: Give & Receive Appreciation
You will have 10 minutes for this exercise, and your facilitator will keep track of time for you.

1. In this exercise, your Round Table will be able to give and receive appreciation to other Round Tables for the expressions of belonging that were shared at the start of class.
2. Your Coordinators will divide each Round Table into 2 equal groups.
   a. Half your group goes to your target Table to receive appreciation for the belonging gifts you brought.
   b. The other half of your group stays at your Round Table to express appreciation to the group from the Round Table that gave you belonging gifts.
   c. Volunteering either to stay at your Table to express appreciation or to visit another Table to receive appreciation helps divide your table for the exercise.
3. Anyone who wants to connect with a target Table, but doesn't get the chance during the exercise, can stay a moment after group.

Belonging Homework: Week 5

Belonging Coordinators
- Email Round Table members with the Round Table Belonging Preferences Worksheet, page 78. You completed this worksheet in the pre-group meeting between the Facilitator and BCs.
- Send an email reminder to Round Table members reminding them to bring an expression of belonging for the other 2 members of their small group – and their coordinator – next week.

Everyone
- Prepare a way to express belonging and appreciation to the other 2 members of your small group and your coordinator. Bring it to class next week.
- Go Shalom Watching! Complete your Shalom Watching Worksheet and bring it with you to class next week, pages 76-77.

Quieting: Shalom for my Soul and Heart
©Copyright E. James Wilder Ph.D. and Ed Khouri, 2009.

Our goal: Quiet the distress our soul and heart feel so that we can return to shalom and appreciation with our relational circuits restored.

Instructions: Honestly share your answers to each question, with all the feeling you can express, out loud with God. If you feel angry, answer the questions on the "Anger" side of your worksheet. If you feel anxious or fearful, answer the questions on the Anxious/Fearful side of the worksheet. If you are feeling very distressed, angry or anxious/fearful, it is a good idea to practice your Shalom for my Body worksheet first. When you have finished, see if you can remember any promises God has made you.

If I am feeling Angry:	If I am feeling Anxious or Fearful
1. What happened that has upset me?	1. What happened that has upset me?
2. What feels so unfair about this situation?	2. What feels threatening about this situation?
Keep telling God what feels unfair about your situation until you are also able to tell God how your body feels right now.	*Keep telling God what feels threatening about your situation until you are also able to tell God how your body feels right now.*
After 5 minutes, if you still feel very angry, focus on any part of your situation that is sad. Tell God how you and others have been hurt in this situation, and how your body feels now. Is there any part of this situation that makes God sad?	*After 5 minutes, if you still feel very anxious or scared, focus on any part of your situation that is sad. Tell God how you and others have been hurt in this situation, and how your body feels now. Is there any part of this situation that makes God sad?*
3. Ask God to show you where He sees you were hurt most. *(Sometimes this is a repeating injury and brings up other hurts.)*	3. Ask God to give you shelter.
4. What is different about this situation now that God and I are looking at things together?	4. What is different about this situation now that God and I are looking at things together?
5. What do I appreciate or long for when God joins me? Share your appreciation with God and tell Him what your longing feels like.	5. What do I appreciate or long for when God joins me? Share your appreciation with God and tell Him what your longing feels like.

Go Shalom, Appreciation and RC Watching

A five-day log of observations about shalom, appreciation and my relational circuits
© Copyright E. James Wilder Ph.D. and Ed Khouri, 2009.

Instructions:
Each day, use this form to keep track of shalom, appreciation and your RCs. Briefly describe when you noticed that shalom, appreciation and your RCs were fading, and how the problem began. Next, place a check next to every statement that describes what happened when you lost shalom, appreciation and your RCs, then place a check next to each step you used to restore them. Finally, write one word that best describes what it felt like emotionally and in your body when you lost shalom, appreciation and your RCs – and when they were restored.

Day 1: When did I notice that my shalom, appreciation and RCs faded? What started these fading?

What happened when I lost shalom, appreciation and my RCs?	
____ Attachment pain was involved.	____ My cravings increased.
____ I lost Godsight.	____ I stopped creating Belonging.
Which of the following steps did I use to restore shalom, appreciation and my RCs?	
____ RC Checklist ____ Shalom for my Body ____ Shalom for my Soul & Heart	
The emotion validated was _____	The comfort was _____
When my shalom, appreciation and RCs faded:	**When shalom, appreciation & RCs were restored:**
The emotion I felt was _____	The emotion I felt was _____
My body felt _____	My body felt _____

Day 2: When did I notice that my shalom, appreciation and RCs faded? What started these fading?

What happened when I lost shalom, appreciation and my RCs?	
____ Attachment pain was involved.	____ My cravings increased.
____ I lost Godsight.	____ I stopped creating Belonging.
Which of the following steps did I use to restore shalom, appreciation and my RCs?	
____ RC Checklist ____ Shalom for my Body ____ Shalom for my Soul & Heart	
The emotion validated was _____	The comfort was _____
When my shalom, appreciation and RCs faded:	**When shalom, appreciation & RCs were restored:**
The emotion I felt was _____	The emotion I felt was _____
My body felt _____	My body felt _____

Day 3: When did I notice that my shalom, appreciation and RCs faded? What started these fading?

What happened when I lost shalom, appreciation and my RCs?		
___ Attachment pain was involved.	___ My cravings increased.	
___ I lost Godsight.	___ I stopped creating Belonging.	
Which of the following steps did I use to restore shalom, appreciation and my RCs?		
___ RC Checklist	___ Shalom for my Body	___ Shalom for my Soul & Heart
The emotion validated was _____	The comfort was _____	
When my shalom, appreciation and RCs faded:	**When shalom, appreciation & RCs were restored:**	
The emotion I felt was _____	The emotion I felt was _____	
My body felt _____	My body felt _____	

Day 4: When did I notice that my shalom, appreciation and RCs faded? What started these fading?

What happened when I lost shalom, appreciation and my RCs?		
___ Attachment pain was involved.	___ My cravings increased.	
___ I lost Godsight.	___ I stopped creating Belonging.	
Which of the following steps did I use to restore shalom, appreciation and my RCs?		
___ RC Checklist	___ Shalom for my Body	___ Shalom for my Soul & Heart
The emotion validated was _____	The comfort was _____	
When my shalom, appreciation and RCs faded:	**When shalom, appreciation & RCs were restored:**	
The emotion I felt was _____	The emotion I felt was _____	
My body felt _____	My body felt _____	

Day 5: When did I notice that my shalom, appreciation and RCs faded? What started these fading?

What happened when I lost shalom, appreciation and my RCs?		
___ Attachment pain was involved.	___ My cravings increased.	
___ I lost Godsight.	___ I stopped creating Belonging.	
Which of the following steps did I use to restore shalom, appreciation and my RCs?		
___ RC Checklist	___ Shalom for my Body	___ Shalom for my Soul & Heart
The emotion validated was _____	The comfort was _____	
When my shalom, appreciation and RCs faded:	**When shalom, appreciation & RCs were restored:**	
The emotion I felt was _____	The emotion I felt was _____	
My body felt _____	My body felt _____	

Coordinators: Round Table Belonging Preferences

(Based on what you have observed so far at your Round Table)
©Copyright E. James Wilder Ph.D. and Ed Khouri, 2009.

Instructions: From what you have observed so far at your Round Table, tell other Coordinators what the favorite way of creating belonging appears to be in your Round Table. Use this list to record the belonging preferences for every Round Table in class.

Email this list to everyone in your Round Table this week.

Belonging Coordinator	Table's Favorite Way To Create Belonging

Notes

Chapter 5: Questions for Further Discussion

Note: The Belonging Goal Checkup on the next page is included as part of questions for further discussion.

1. From what we learned in this week's lesson, answer the question "Why do people like you?" What happens in your relationships when you or others amplify distress? To answer this question, think about 5 relationships that are important to you. What happens in each of these when you - or they - amplify negative emotions? How does this affect belonging?

2. How do you think quieting could affect your relationships with God and others who are important to you? Be specific.

3. Have you ever seen a relationship in which someone was able to make a relationship bigger and more important than a problem? Think about everyone involved, including you. What happened to everyone's RCs?

4. Were your RCs stronger after doing the Shalom for my Body and Shalom for my Soul and Heart exercises in class this week? Were your RCs working better - or did they stay the same? Be specific.

5. Did you practice your RC checks and the Shalom for my Body and Shalom for my Soul and Heart exercises at home this week? How did these affect your RCs and ability to create belonging? Be specific. What happened that caused your RCs to fade, and what happened when your RCs were more active?

6. As you practiced the Shalom for my Soul and Heart exercise, were you able to recognize the validation and comfort you received? Describe them.

7. When you did the Shalom for my Soul and Heart exercise, what was different about your situation when you and Jesus were looking at the situation together?

8. When we don't receive validation and comfort, denial and fear grow. Can you think about times in which you did not receive validation and comfort - and denial and fear grew? How has this affected belonging?

9. How can validation and comfort help us change the kinds of things we say to ourselves and our behavior? What kinds of things would be different in your life if you experienced validation and comfort regularly when you were upset?

Notes

Belonging Goal Checkup:

Instructions:
Here are some of the Belonging Goals we started with in our first week. Place a check mark next to each goal that you've made progress in since we started! When you have completed this checklist, share your progress and celebrate your success together! Then, make a list of the areas that you would like to practice to better improve your Belonging skills.

- ❏ To recognize why belonging is something we create around us.
- ❏ To be part of creating a belonging-friendly environment.
- ❏ To discover my own unique style for creating belonging, and learn to express it!
- ❏ To learn how stories can create belonging – and learn to tell them!
- ❏ To learn to recognize when my RCs are off – and how to turn them back on again – so that I am able to perceive God's presence.
- ❏ To perceive God's presence and interact with Him.
- ❏ To learn belonging skills like appreciation, quieting and telling joyful stories.
- ❏ To improve maturity skills that help me create more belonging.
- ❏ To learn how my feelings – and learning to express them appropriately – can help create belonging.
- ❏ To spread belonging through our stories.

Areas I would like to practice:

Notes

Notes

Belonging Chapter 6:

THE PAIN OF NOT BELONGING:
ATTACHMENT PAIN LEAVES ME FEELING ALONE AND REPLACES BELONGING.

Group Opens:
• Ask a volunteer to open the group with prayer.

Belonging exercise: Star Card Class Exercise
This is a 10 minute exercise, and your facilitator will keep track of time for you.

1. Remain at your Round Table for this exercise.

2. Your Facilitator will give each of you Star Cards.

3. During class tonight, give a Star Card to every person you see creating belonging, especially if they are creating belonging with style.

4. When you give someone a Star Card, tell him or her:
   a. What you saw her/him do that created belonging.
   b. How that made you feel (appreciation moment).

5. If you have any cards left over, take them with you and give them to people you see creating belonging this week.

Belonging exercise: Shalom Watching Report!
You will have 10 minutes for this exercise, and your facilitator will keep track of time for you.

1. Break into groups of 3 from your Round Table, and follow your facilitator's instructions.

2. Use your Shalom Watching Worksheet to guide you, and share your Shalom Watching experiences from this past week with the members of your small group, pages 76-77.

3. Use these helpful guidelines as you share your Shalom Watching experiences with your small group:
   a. Did anyone return to shalom and appreciation with his/her RCs active using the Belonging quieting steps we've learned in class?
   b. What Belonging quieting steps did you use?
   c. Were you able to recognize the validation and comfort you received?
   d. Describe the emotions and body sensations you felt before and after you returned to shalom and appreciation with your RCs active.

4. You will have 10 minutes, and your facilitator will keep track of time for you as you share.

5. Important reminder: Don't overwhelm each other with intensity as you share your Shalom Watching Report.
   a. Reports that are overly intense may overwhelm the other members of your small group and cause their RCs to shut down.
   b. It is helpful to share Shalom Watching experiences that are mildly - moderately intense.

DID YOU GO SHALOM WATCHING THIS WEEK?
What happened, and how did you restore shalom, appreciation and your RCs?

Belonging Exercise: Shalom Watching Prayer
You will have 10 minutes for this exercise, and your facilitator will keep track of time for you.

1. Return to your Round Table after you share your Shalom Watching Report.

2. Take the next 10 minutes to pray for each other at your Round Table.

3. Pray that each of you will be helped to release your ability to create belonging and increase shalom, appreciation and your RC activity.

Please start the Belonging DVD for this week's lesson.

Belonging Teaching: Attachment pain leaves me feeling alone and replaces belonging.

What does "Belonging" look like?
• Belonging is the joy we create around us!

Belonging is Training!

Weekly Bible Story: Jesus, Lazarus and Attachment Pain
• Staying relational and acting like myself when I feel attachment pain.

Attachment Pain:
• Is distress at Level 1 of the Control Center and is the deepest level of pain.
• Is the kind of pain I feel when I've lost appreciation and shalom, and my RCs fade.

Attachment Pain is the kind of distress I feel when:
• I don't feel connected to anyone.
• A person that I have been connected to is no longer present.
• There is distance between me and someone I've been connected with.
• I don't know where I belong or have someone to belong to.

Attachment Pain:
• Can affect relationships with both God and others.
• Is sub-cortical – below conscious awareness.
• Is not observed or controlled by conscious thought.

Intensity
• Attachment pain is so intense, that everything in us tries to make the pain go away by any means necessary.
• Attachment pain can pervade and affect every area of life.
• Everything hurts and feels more intense!

RC Shutdown
• Attachment pain is both hidden and very powerful.
• We feel it, but may not recognize, understand or know what we are feeling.

> ### ATTACHMENT PAIN HURTS DEEPLY.
> *Attachment Pain is the kind of distress we feel when we've lost shalom and appreciation - and our RCs start to shut down. Without life-giving connections with God and others, we feel isolated and alone, and when we don't feel connected to anyone, or experience distance in relationships with people we love, we feel attachment pain.*

Attachment Pain is one of the main reasons our RCs shut down.
- Attachment Pain also makes it very difficult for us to live in shalom and appreciation.

When we are in attachment pain and our capacity is overwhelmed, we may blast others with the problems and pain we feel.

The Blast:
- When we blast others, we overwhelm their capacity, and they can no longer stay connected with us.
- This will always make pain and problems bigger than relationship.

Our attachment pain grows:
- Before long, we find ourselves craving relief from our distress.
- But because our RCs are down, we can't engage with others to enjoy the connections we crave.

Cravings
- Attachment pain is often felt in the form of cravings.
- More about this in Week 8!

The attachment pain trap:
- The brain will not accept a substitute or replacement bond.
- It only wants the person it is already attached to.
- This is why hoping to "be loved out of" our attachment pain becomes so toxic to us – and to others.
- Community and spiritual family can only give us enough strength to feel and acknowledge attachment pain – and learn to suffer well.
- They cannot heal our attachment pain for us.
- Hoping to be loved out of attachment pain, or trying to find a relationship that will end attachment pain, are toxic hopes.
- Only God can heal the deepest levels of attachment pain. (Healing Module)

You can't find the "perfect relationship" that will love you out of your attachment pain.

Toxic Pain:
- Attachment pain can cause unhealthy attachments to grow, even when we don't want them to and agree that they shouldn't.
- Attachment pain makes good solutions and relationships turn sour or sexual.
- It also drives many addictions like cutting, food and sex.

Attachment pain distorts boundaries:
- It assumes responsibility for the decisions, behaviors, feelings and responsibilities that others should reasonably carry for themselves.
- Codependent rescues, "ministry" and over-involvement in the lives of others often follow.
- Burnout, chronic immaturity and greater attachment pain follow.

CODEPENDENCY IS ROOTED IN ATTACHMENT PAIN.
Hoping to be loved out of attachment pain, trying to love someone out of attachment pain, or trying to maintain a relationship to avoid attachment pain all cause us to assume responsibility for the behaviors, feelings and responsibilities of others - and lead to the development and growth of destructive, codependent relationships.

Notes

How about a "quick fix?"
- Quick fixes and "miracle" formulas or breakthroughs are sometimes mistakenly seen as the way to deal with attachment pain.
- Long-term healing relationships with God and others are wrongly seen as unnecessary, unimportant, "Plan B" or "unspiritual."

Restoration:
- Learning to identify attachment pain can help us recognize the need to restore shalom, appreciation, and RCs.
- Then, we can use our Belonging quieting steps to return to appreciation and shalom with our RCs fully active.

We can stop living under the tyranny of attachment pain and strong cravings.
- We can become relational again, live in shalom and appreciation, and start creating belonging!

Belonging Exercise: My Attachment Pain Checklist
Your facilitator will lead you through this 10 minute exercise.

1. Remain at your Round Table as your facilitator leads you through the Unrecognized Attachment Pain Checklist.

2. Locate the Unrecognized Attachment Pain Checklist in Chapter 6 of your workbook, pages 89-91.

3. As your facilitator walks you through the checklist, and answers any questions about it that you may have, mark each statement on the checklist that applies to you.

4. You do not have to share your checklist with anyone else.

5. You will have 10 minutes for this exercise.

Belonging exercise: RC Check and Shalom for my Body
You will have 1 minute for a quick RC Check using your short form, and 4 minutes for the Shalom for my Body exercise.

1. Remain at your Round Table as your facilitator leads the class through an RC Check and Shalom for my Body exercise.

2. Check your relational circuits using the Shalom for my Body Short Form
   - ❏ I just want to make a problem, person or feeling go away.
   - ❏ I don't want to listen to what others feel or say.
   - ❏ My mind is "locked onto" something upsetting.
   - ❏ I don't want to be connected to? (someone I usually like)
   - ❏ I just want to get away, or fight or I freeze.
   - ❏ I more aggressively interrogate, judge and fix others.

3. When you have finished the RC Check, your facilitator will lead the class in the Shalom for my Body exercise.
   a. Set the timing right with the verse based on Psalm 56:3: "Whenever I am afraid I will trust in you O Lord."
   b. Move your body (4 moves).
   c. Breathe and scrunch.
   d. Yawn left and right
   e. Knock to wake up your attachment center
   f. Get the sympathetic and parasympathetic synchronized with each other (change speeds).

Belonging Exercise: Grow My Appreciation

You will have a total of 20 minutes for this exercise, and your facilitator will track time in each part.

1. Form groups of 3 with members of your Round Table, and follow your facilitator's instructions.

2. In this exercise, you will grow your appreciation by telling a Level 4+ Story about a person that you appreciate.

3. Use the Appreciation Story Worksheet on page 92 of your workbook to prepare your story. You will have 5 minutes to complete the worksheet.

4. Next, follow your facilitator's instructions, and take turns sharing your story with the other members of your small group.
   a. Everyone will have 3 minutes to tell their story, and 2 minutes for feedback.
   b. As you give feedback, remember to encourage each other for every element of a 4+ Story that members included in their story. Your feedback can also help members recognize elements of a 4+ Story that may have been missing. Feedback is always positive and encouraging, and is never harsh or critical.

5. Your facilitator will keep track of time for you.
   a. Each group member has 5 minutes to tell a story and receive feedback.
   b. Your facilitator will let you know when it is time for another member of your group to begin telling a story.

Belonging Homework: Week 6

Belonging Coordinators:
- Send everyone in your Round Table an email thanking them for their expression of belonging this week.

Everyone:
Star Cards: If you have any Star Cards left over, hand them out during the week.

Go Shalom Watching
- This week, use your Shalom Watching Worksheet daily to notice when attachment pain causes you to lose shalom and appreciation, and causes your RCs to fade, pages 94-95.
- Then, use the steps you've learned so far to get your RCs back on!

Continue to pray for others from your Round Table.
- Pray that they will be fully released in their ability to create belonging, restore their RCs and return to shalom & appreciation.

REMEMBER:
THE ATTACHMENT PAIN CHECKLIST IS A POWERFUL BELONGING TOOL.

Learning to use the Attachment Pain Checklist can help us learn to recognize attachment pain before it becomes too intense, damages our relationships and leads to cravings that are simply too strong for us to handle.

Once we recognize attachment pain, we can practice our Belonging Quieting Steps to return to shalom and appreciation with our RCs active. Instead of isolation, increased pain, damaged relationships and intense cravings, I can create Belonging!

Notes

Wise Thoughts about Attachment Pain and the Unrecognized Attachment Pain Checklist
©Copyright E. James Wilder Ph.D. and Ed Khouri, 2009.

Wise Thought One:
This attachment pain inventory is intended for use in conjunction with the training that accompanies the Belonging module. Please do not use this inventory to help someone recognize attachment pain without adequate training to help them resolve attachment pain.

Wise Thought Two:
The presence of one or more of these indicators by themselves does not necessarily indicate the presence of attachment pain. People hurt for a lot of reasons. Attachment pain adds intensity to all other issues. Even a stomach ache caused by green apples hurts more when you are alone in the world with no one who cares or when your mother does not come. The intensified feeling you experience because you are all alone is one of the biggest indicators of attachment pain. It helps to become aware of your attachment pain, and it will also help to take care of your stomach ache!

Wise Thought Three:
Attachment pain itself is sub cortical, which means that it is not directly observed or controlled by conscious thoughts. We need to observe the signs of attachment pain and recognize its source. This is like being sleepy. One day it is caused by a hard day's work, another time by too little sleep, another time by feeling overwhelmed by demands on you, another time by your allergy medicine and yet another because you are starting to freeze to death. Not all signs are serious or potentially hazardous – but the failure to pay attention to the overwhelming desire to fall asleep in very cold weather can lead to death. Likewise, failure to recognize the signs of attachment pain can cause serious damage to our lives, relationships and emotions. Attachment pain is something you should consider when any of the symptoms on this list are becoming overwhelming and there is a chance that you have lost love or joy in your life about the time the symptoms started.

Wise Thought Four:
Attachment pain is different from other pains in that our brains does not "get over" the loss of people and things we are attached to like it would an injury. If I lose my cheeseburger, another cheeseburger of equal quality will do. If I lose my beloved, I can still hurt about it years later, and all kinds of things can remind me of the loss. Attachment pain does not have to come from a recent loss to have returned just now.

Wise thought Five:
Attachment pain is the major reason we stop creating belonging around us. It hurts to lose those we want to attach and belong with, or to be rejected by them. Attachment pain is also the cause of "hoarding belonging," which means that we are trying to keep people, groups and places to ourselves. Holding onto harmful relationship patterns is caused by a panicked effort to avoid attachment pain.

Wise Thought Six:
Attachment pain is often felt in the form of cravings. When we substitute thrills and things (in Thriving we call these BEEPS) for attachment joy with people and God, we start having attachment pain when we can't find what we crave. These cravings become unmanageable monsters once our brain's relational circuits get turned off. Many people try to avoid attachment pain by living with their relational circuits off much of the time, and this makes them very vulnerable to cravings and BEEPS. (See the Belonging Relational Circuits Checklist, pages 50-51, for further help.)

The Unrecognized Attachment Pain Checklist

©Copyright E. James Wilder Ph.D. and Ed Khouri, 2009

General Signs of Attachment Pain

- ❑ I feel the loss of someone special.
- ❑ I feel homesick.
- ❑ I don't feel much joy.
    - ❑ I feel irritable, restless or bored.
    - ❑ I feel blue/depressed.
    - ❑ I feel alone, isolated or lonely.
    - ❑ I don't have much energy for life or others.
- ❑ I like to be a "lone ranger."
    - ❑ I don't like to join.
    - ❑ I don't like commitments.
    - ❑ I don't like people getting close and depending on me.
- ❑ Something bothers me but I'm not sure what.
    - ❑ I feel frustrated, confused and don't know what the problem is.
    - ❑ I can't seem to settle down.
    - ❑ My thoughts race.
    - ❑ I can't sleep.
    - ❑ I can't rest.
    - ❑ I want to "turn it off" but I can't.
    - ❑ I am focused on minor details.
    - ❑ I feel overwhelmed/tense/anxious but don't know why.
- ❑ I have to distract myself.
    - ❑ I have almost no alone or quiet time.
    - ❑ I have TV, phone, iPod, entertainment or distractions going almost all the time.
    - ❑ I find myself suddenly just doing something to keep busy.
- ❑ Fears control my social life at times.
    - ❑ I do not want to risk love, groups, rejection or belonging again.
    - ❑ I fear speaking or being in front of a group.
- ❑ I keep losing control in areas of my life.
    - ❑ My willpower and choices just don't seem to keep me doing the right thing.
    - ❑ I repeatedly do, think or feel things I am ashamed or afraid to tell others – especially those close to me.
    - ❑ I feel like I can't stand up for myself in relationships, and feel like my emotions and desires are getting overrun by others.
- ❑ I am trying to justify in my mind why these questions don't apply to me.

Notes

- ❑ My emotions are too intense ("over the top") sometimes.
    - ❑ Some things upset me more than they should.
    - ❑ I can't feel close to people when I or they are feeling at least one of the big six feelings. It seems that those same feelings are harmful to relationships.
        - ❑ Anger
        - ❑ Fear
        - ❑ Shame
        - ❑ Sadness
        - ❑ Disgust
        - ❑ Hopeless Despair
    - ❑ The way I handle one of these big six feelings is damaging my relationships.
    - ❑ How someone near me handles one of these big six feelings is damaging our relationship.
    - ❑ Things feel like a bigger deal than it seems they should be.
    - ❑ Everything is a big deal.
    - ❑ I am feeling more resentful.
    - ❑ I feel almost continuously sad.
    - ❑ I feel like crying for no reason.
    - ❑ I find myself fantasizing/daydreaming.
- ❑ I have made questionable judgment calls.
    - ❑ What seem to be good ideas to me end up putting me in compromising positions.
    - ❑ People often tell me that my judgment is off, but I don't think it is or insist it isn't.
    - ❑ I upset some people so that I do not upset other people.
    - ❑ I have overspent my way into debt.
    - ❑ I have lapses of judgment or increased conflicts about my judgment with people close to me.
    - ❑ I have hidden relationships.
    - ❑ I disregard important care (like diet restrictions or exercise) that impacts my health.
    - ❑ I smoke/chew.
- ❑ I have intensified physical or health concerns.
    - ❑ I am always checking and afraid of gaining weight.
    - ❑ I am greatly bothered by pains that do not respond to treatment.
    - ❑ I am much more concerned about my physical symptoms than my health care providers.
    - ❑ Much of my mental energy is spent on what could be going wrong in my body.
    - ❑ I have tried everything for this pain and nothing is working.
    - ❑ I keep trying to increase my medication levels even though they don't solve the problem.

Relational Signs of Attachment Pain

Short term relational signs my attachment pain is increasing:

- ❑ I start becoming impatient.
- ❑ I get angry more easily and/or it is stronger than it used to be.
- ❑ I start blaming others (or want to).
- ❑ I think my life would be much better if I could just find another relationship to make me happy.
- ❑ I don't like it when people tell me that I overreact to things.
- ❑ I start to wish you would hurt like I do, or I think of ways to make you feel pain.
- ❑ Pains in my body I can usually deal with become "too much" and I get focused on ways to make them stop.
- ❑ My fears and worries take over.
- ❑ My voice has an edge.
- ❑ I start warning people to "watch out" and not upset me now.

Long Term Relational Signs of Attachment Pain

Long term relational signs my attachment pain is increasing:

- ❑ I compromise myself and my standards to keep people with me longer.
- ❑ My friends or other close relationships are becoming increasingly less important to me.
- ❑ I am always wanting to find relationships.
- ❑ My relationship with God and important people in my life feels unsatisfying.
- ❑ I often dread the thought of someone else's feelings getting hurt.
- ❑ I spend a lot of mental energy keeping track of the people I think can make me feel better.
- ❑ I keep taking care of others and make excuses for why they don't take care of themselves.
- ❑ People I love keep making a big deal out of problems that don't seem that big or important to me.
- ❑ I feel numb and cold inside about the people close to me.
- ❑ I am leading a double life.
- ❑ There are parts of me that I don't share or talk about with anyone (including God).
- ❑ I'm in an abusive relationship, but I am afraid to let go of the relationship.

Note: The presence of one or more of these indicators by themselves does not necessarily indicate the presence of attachment pain.

Notes

Belonging 4+ Story Appreciation Worksheet

©Copyright E. James Wilder Ph.D. and Ed Khouri, 2009.

Telling my appreciation story the 4+ way

❑ This story has a moderate feeling level and is not too intense.

❑ I do not need to be guarded about this story and can talk freely about it.

❑ This story is about me (autobiographical) and I am involved in telling the story.

❑ I show genuine emotions on my face and in my voice when telling the story.

❑ I keep eye contact with my listeners while storytelling.

❑ I include words for my emotions.

❑ I describe what my body felt like.

❑ I describe appreciation enough for others to know how it feels.

❑ I say what is it like me to do when I am creating belonging once again.

❑ This story begins and ends with me feeling appreciation.

Give a brief description of my situation:

Use these emotional feeling words for my story:

Include this description of how my body felt:

Say what I appreciated:

Tell the effect of appreciation on my desire to create belonging (share good things with others):

To Grow Even More Appreciation:

Now that I've told my appreciation story, and listened as my small group shared their stories with me, are there any other appreciation memories that come to mind? Make a list of each in the space provided below. You won't be sharing these in class today, but you can use this list to remind you of appreciation memories the next time you want to tell an appreciation story.

As you list new memories, you may find it helpful to give each memory a name that helps you remember the appreciation moment. For example, for a really great Christmas memory, you may just want to write: "Christmas at Paul's House."

More Appreciation Memories:

Go Shalom, Appreciation and RC Watching

A five-day log of observations about shalom, appreciation and my relational circuits
© Copyright E. James Wilder Ph.D. and Ed Khouri, 2009.

Instructions:
Each day, use this form to keep track of shalom, appreciation and your RCs. Briefly describe when you noticed that shalom, appreciation and your RCs were fading, and how the problem began. Next, place a check next to every statement that describes what happened when you lost shalom, appreciation and your RCs, then place a check next to each step you used to restore them. Finally, write one word that best describes what it felt like emotionally and in your body when you lost shalom, appreciation and your RCs – and when they were restored.

Day 1: When did I notice that my shalom, appreciation and RCs faded? What started these fading?

What happened when I lost shalom, appreciation and my RCs?		
___ Attachment pain was involved.	___ My cravings increased.	
___ I lost Godsight.	___ I stopped creating Belonging.	
Which of the following steps did I use to restore shalom, appreciation and my RCs?		
___ RC Checklist	___ Shalom for my Body	___ Shalom for my Soul & Heart
The emotion validated was _____	The comfort was _____	
When my shalom, appreciation and RCs faded:	**When shalom, appreciation & RCs were restored:**	
The emotion I felt was _____	The emotion I felt was _____	
My body felt _____	My body felt _____	

Day 2: When did I notice that my shalom, appreciation and RCs faded? What started these fading?

What happened when I lost shalom, appreciation and my RCs?		
___ Attachment pain was involved.	___ My cravings increased.	
___ I lost Godsight.	___ I stopped creating Belonging.	
Which of the following steps did I use to restore shalom, appreciation and my RCs?		
___ RC Checklist	___ Shalom for my Body	___ Shalom for my Soul & Heart
The emotion validated was _____	The comfort was _____	
When my shalom, appreciation and RCs faded:	**When shalom, appreciation & RCs were restored:**	
The emotion I felt was _____	The emotion I felt was _____	
My body felt _____	My body felt _____	

Day 3: When did I notice that my shalom, appreciation and RCs faded? What started these fading?

What happened when I lost shalom, appreciation and my RCs?		
___ Attachment pain was involved.	___ My cravings increased.	
___ I lost Godsight.	___ I stopped creating Belonging.	
Which of the following steps did I use to restore shalom, appreciation and my RCs?		
___ RC Checklist	___ Shalom for my Body	___ Shalom for my Soul & Heart
The emotion validated was _____	The comfort was _____	
When my shalom, appreciation and RCs faded:	When shalom, appreciation & RCs were restored:	
The emotion I felt was _____	The emotion I felt was _____	
My body felt _____	My body felt _____	

Day 4: When did I notice that my shalom, appreciation and RCs faded? What started these fading?

What happened when I lost shalom, appreciation and my RCs?		
___ Attachment pain was involved.	___ My cravings increased.	
___ I lost Godsight.	___ I stopped creating Belonging.	
Which of the following steps did I use to restore shalom, appreciation and my RCs?		
___ RC Checklist	___ Shalom for my Body	___ Shalom for my Soul & Heart
The emotion validated was _____	The comfort was _____	
When my shalom, appreciation and RCs faded:	When shalom, appreciation & RCs were restored:	
The emotion I felt was _____	The emotion I felt was _____	
My body felt _____	My body felt _____	

Day 5: When did I notice that my shalom, appreciation and RCs faded? What started these fading?

What happened when I lost shalom, appreciation and my RCs?		
___ Attachment pain was involved.	___ My cravings increased.	
___ I lost Godsight.	___ I stopped creating Belonging.	
Which of the following steps did I use to restore shalom, appreciation and my RCs?		
___ RC Checklist	___ Shalom for my Body	___ Shalom for my Soul & Heart
The emotion validated was _____	The comfort was _____	
When my shalom, appreciation and RCs faded:	When shalom, appreciation & RCs were restored:	
The emotion I felt was _____	The emotion I felt was _____	
My body felt _____	My body felt _____	

Notes

Chapter 6: Questions for Further Discussion

1. What have you been learning in Belonging about your own style of creating belonging? How do you like to create belonging? What are your favorite ways to create belonging in our belonging class - and outside of it? Be specific.

2. Did you use the Shalom Watching Worksheet this week? What kinds of things caused your RCs to fade this week? Were you able to restore your RCs and return to appreciation and shalom?

3. What is attachment pain, and why is it so intense? Why do we begin to experience attachment pain when our RCs start to fade?

4. Why do cravings become more intense when we feel attachment pain? What happens to your cravings when you feel attachment pain?

5. How can community help us heal from attachment pain? What kinds of thing could a community do to help you deal with your attachment pain? What kinds of things could a community do that would not be helpful?

6. Why is hoping to find another person or community to "love" us out of our attachment pain so toxic to us and to them? Have you ever pursued a person, relationship or community in the hopes that they would end your attachment pain? What happened?

7. Please answer the following as completely as you can. Has attachment pain ever:
   a. Caused unhealthy attachments to grow in your own life?
   b. Caused a good relationship to become sour or sexual?
   c. Fueled an addiction or added energy to it?

8. How has attachment pain distorted boundaries and led to the development of codependent relationships in your life? Please describe at least 3 of these relationships, how attachment pain was involved, and what boundaries were distorted.

9. When you completed that attachment pain checklist, what seemed to be the best indicators that you were feeling or experiencing attachment pain? What were the relational signs of attachment pain that you noticed?

Notes

Notes

Belonging Chapter 7:

GODSIGHT RESTORES BELONGING AND MAKES RELATIONSHIPS BIGGER THAN PROBLEMS.

Group Opens:
- Ask a volunteer to open the group with prayer.

Belonging Exercise: Random Acts Of Creating Belonging
This is a 25 minute exercise that has 3 parts, and your facilitator will keep track of time for you.

Introduction (5 Minutes)
1. Please remain at your Round Tables as your facilitator introduces this exercise.
2. This week, your goal is to try out your style of creating belonging on an unsuspecting person at church.
3. This should be something you enjoy doing – or would like to try – that will make someone at church happy to be there, want to come back and want to see if you are there again.

Deciding how (10 Minutes)
1. Form small groups of three from your Round Table.
2. Decide how each of you will express your "random act of creating belonging around you" at church.
3. You can use ideas you've heard in class, as well as the list of the ways everyone likes to give and receive belonging that your Coordinator emailed you.
4. Your facilitator will keep time for you.

Share your plan (10 Minutes)
1. Rejoin your Round Table for this part of the exercise, and share how you want to express your "random act of creating belonging around you."
2. As you each share your goals, your Belonging Coordinator will use the worksheet on page 107 to write them down, and send you an email reminder during the week.
3. While you are at your Round Table, express belonging to your Coordinator.
4. Your facilitator will keep time for you.

Belonging Exercise: Shalom Watching Report!
This is a 10 minute exercise, and your facilitator will keep track of time for you.

1. Break into groups of 3 from your Round Table, and follow your facilitator's instructions.
2. Use your Shalom Watching Worksheet to guide you, and share your Shalom Watching experiences from this past week with the members of your small group, pages 94-95.

> ### THIS WEEK: TRY A RANDOM ACT OF CREATING BELONGING!
> *Try out your own style of creating belonging on an unsuspecting person at church.*

Notes

3. Use these helpful guidelines as you share your Shalom Watching experiences with your small group:
   a. Did anyone return to shalom and appreciation with his/her RCs active using the Belonging quieting steps we've learned in class?
   b. Did anyone notice attachment pain this week?
   c. What Belonging quieting steps did you use?
   d. Were you able to recognize the validation and comfort you received?
   e. Describe the emotions and body sensations you felt before and after you returned to shalom and appreciation with your RCs active.

4. You will have 10 minutes, and your facilitator will keep track of time for you as you share.

5. Important reminder: Don't overwhelm each other with intensity as you share your Shalom Watching Report.
   a. Reports that are overly intense may overwhelm the other members of your small group and cause their RCs to shut down.
   b. It is helpful to share Shalom Watching experiences that are minimally to moderately intense.

Please start the Belonging DVD for this week's lesson.

Belonging Teaching: Godsight: Making our relationships bigger than our problems

What does "Belonging" look like?
• Belonging is the joy we create around us!

Belonging is Training!

Weekly Bible Story: Jesus and the woman at the well
• Acting like myself and finding my true identity.

Godsight is invaluable.
• Godsight is learning to see people, situations and ourselves like God does.
• Godsight restores belonging and makes relationships bigger than problems.

Godsight:
• Godsight allows us to see God, ourselves, others and the problem like He does.
• Godsight helps restore us to shalom and appreciation, and reactivates our relational circuits.
• This always gives us the perspective to see the relationship as more important than the challenges and problems.

Jesus makes relationships bigger than problems.
• If we confess our failures and malfunctions to Him, He cleanses and restores us to relationship with Him.

When we restore our relationship to Him, He moves the problem out of the way so that we can enjoy relationship with Him.
• He makes relationship more important than our problems, mistakes and malfunctions!

JESUS ALWAYS MAKES RELATIONSHIP BIGGER THAN OUR PROBLEMS.
If we confess our failures and malfunctions to Him, He cleanses us and restores us to relationship with Him. He moves the problem out of the way so we can enjoy relationship with Him - before we even know how to fix the problems!

Godsight doesn't ignore problems.
- It just sees relationship as bigger and more important than the problems.

He's just solution-centered.
- God is more interested in building joy with us (which helps us heal) than He is in punishing us for having the problem.

Godsight, shalom and appreciation.
- Godsight helps us live in shalom internally and in relationship with God.
- When we see things from God's perspective, it's easier to find people and things to appreciate.
- Godsight, shalom and appreciation keep our RCs active, and help us heal and grow relationally.

Godsight, shalom and appreciation also reduce the intensity of our cravings for "Belonging Substitutes!"

So, when we start to see and value relationships with Godsight,
- Our relational circuits will be active.

With Godsight, appreciation, shalom and our RCs fully active, we are free to:
- Make relationships more important than the problems in our relationships!
- Discover life and relationships from God's point of view.
- Stay relational with each other – even in the midst of conflict.
- Find the comfort and strength to overcome cravings and attachment pain.

Without Godsight:
- We experience attachment pain because our RCs are not working very well.
- We make problems bigger than relationships, and overwhelm others with the intensity of our emotions.

It won't be long until people avoid me, shun me, punish me, ignore me or tune me out.

And with my relational circuits off, my cravings will become much more intense!

Godsight helps me keep my RCs on so I can live in shalom and appreciation, and keep my relationships bigger than my problems.
- Let's get ready for Godsight practice!

Belonging Exercise: Telling Godsight Stories to Create Belonging
This is a 25 minute exercise that has 2 parts. Your facilitator will guide you through the exercise and keep track of time for you.

Introduction:

1. Please remain at your Round Table for both parts of this exercise.

2. To start, you will need your Week 7 Exercise Worksheet, which is located in chapter 7 of your workbook, page 104.

GOD IS NOT BLIND, IS NOT IN DENIAL AND DOESN'T IGNORE PROBLEMS.

God just sees relationships as bigger and as more important than our problems. He is more interested in connecting with us so we can experience His love and joy than He is in punishing us for having problems that we simply don't know how to solve!

Notes

3. This exercise has 2 parts:
   a. In Part 1, follow your facilitator's instructions as she or he leads you through the first half of the exercise and worksheet.
   b. In Part 2, you will have the opportunity to share and discuss answers to the questions on the second half of your worksheet in your Round Tables.
4. You will have 25 minutes to finish both parts.

Part 1: Godsight (15 Minutes)

1. Your facilitator will guide you through this part of the exercise.

2. Write down and spend 3 minutes remembering a "5-bar moment" or a time from your appreciation list where you felt God was giving you a gift of help, beauty, joy or belonging.
   a. Your facilitator will remind you that a "5-bar moment" is a time when we felt very close to Jesus.
   b. Just as we have a strong connection on a cell phone with signal strength of 5 bars, a "5-bar moment" refers to a time when we had a very strong connection with Jesus or a very strong sense of His presence.
   c. 5-bar moments and appreciation memories help activate our brain's RCs.
3. Use the spaces on your worksheet to write down the answers to the questions you ask Jesus.
4. Your facilitator will keep track of time for you, and let you know when it's time to move on to the second part of the exercise.

Part 2: Telling Godsight Stories to Create Belonging. (15 Minutes)

1. In your Round Tables, discuss and write your answers to the questions on your worksheet.
2. As you work, pay attention to the answers you wrote down in the Godsight exercise on the first part of the worksheet.
3. Your facilitator will keep track of time for you.

Belonging Exercise: Belonging Rewards
This is a 5 minute exercise, and your facilitator will keep track of time for you.

1. You can remain at your Round Table for this exercise.
2. Help your facilitator award tonight's Belonging Gifts by answering the question: "Who did a great job creating belonging during this exercise?"
3. You can nominate anyone at your Round Table who did a good job creating belonging during the exercise.
4. Your facilitator will award belonging gifts, and the class will help him or her decide who receives today's gifts.
5. Your facilitator will keep track of time for you.

Belonging Homework Assignment: Making Relationships Bigger than Problems Worksheet.
This is an 8 minute exercise to explain and review this week's homework assignment. Your facilitator will explain a new worksheet and review your other homework assignments with you.

Instructions:
Find the Making Relationships Bigger than Problems Worksheet located in Chapter 7, pages 105-106, of your workbook, and follow along as your facilitator explains how to complete it. To complete your worksheet, follow these instructions:

1. Your worksheet has 2 pages.
   a. The first page provides you space to make a list of 10 situations where you feel like someone is a problem or someone thinks you have a problem. The steps for creating belonging in spite of the problem are listed on the bottom of the first page of your worksheet.
   b. The second page provides space for you to begin to work practical steps to help make relationships bigger than problems, by answering the question: "How will I create belonging in spite of this problem so I continue to act like my relational self?"

2. Page 1 Instructions:
   a. Think of a situation where you feel like someone is a problem or someone thinks that you have a problem.
   b. Use the spaces on your worksheet to make a list of 10 of these situations.
   c. When you are finished, pick the least intense one to start.
   d. It is much easier to learn this process and train with a mildly intense situation than it is with a very intense situation.

3. Page 2 Instructions:
   a. Start with the least intense situation you've chosen from your list, and describe it briefly under the "Here is my problem with someone important to me" section of the page.
   b. The 7 Steps on this page will help you answer the question: How will I create belonging in spite of this problem, and continue to act like my relational self?"
   c. Use the spaces provided and write your answers at each step of the process.
   d. Remember: new training patterns take time, so go slow – slower – even slower with this process.

Belonging Homework: Week 7

Belonging Coordinators
- Send all BCs and everyone in your Round Table an email with a copy of the "Random Acts of Creating Belonging Worksheet" you completed with your Round Table in class today, page 107.

Everyone:

Random acts of creating belonging
- Try your "random act of creating belonging around you" at church this week.
- If people ask you why you did your random act of creating belonging, smile and say, "It is just something I like doing and I am learning more about making this feel like home in the Belonging class I am taking."

Complete your "Relationships Bigger than Problems" Worksheet, pages 105-106.
- Remember: Choose the least intense situation from your list.
- Go slow. New training patterns take time.

Go Shalom Watching
- This week, use your Shalom Watching Worksheet to track your experiences with shalom appreciation, and your RCs, pages 108-109.
- This week, be sure and include your observations about both attachment pain and Godsight.
- Then, use the steps you've learned so far to get your RCs back on!

GODSIGHT IS ALWAYS RELATIONAL.

With Godsight, our RCs are active, and we can see ourselves, others and our situations like God does. This helps me make my relationships bigger and more important to me than the problems I have in those relationships!

Belonging Week 7 Class Exercise Worksheet
Copyright E. James Wilder Ph.D. and Ed Khouri 2009.

Godsight Exercise:
Your Facilitator will guide you through this exercise. Write down and spend 3 minutes remembering a 5-bar moment or a time from your appreciation list where you felt God was giving you a gift of help, beauty, joy or belonging.

After remembering God's closeness, I ask Jesus "How do you see me right now" and write down any thoughts that come to my mind.

I ask a second question, "What style for creating belonging did you put in me?" Write down any thoughts that come to my mind.

Round Table Discussion: Telling Godsight Stories to Create Belonging

1. How would I need to tell Godsight stories to create belonging?

2. Could I tell a Godsight story that would keep others from wanting to belong with me? How?

3. What Godsight stories have I heard? How did Jesus create belonging for me and others through those stories?

4. Who can I tell my Godsight stories to who has not heard them before?
    A. Tell a 5-bar moment.
    B. Tell my appreciation for how Jesus sees me.
    C. Tell how God has changed my style of belonging.
    D. Make a plan to tell someone outside my Belonging group this week. Who?

Making Relationships Bigger than Problems Worksheet
Copyright E. James Wilder Ph.D. and Ed Khouri 2009.

Part 1: Identifying a relationship and a problem to start working on.
Think of a situation where you feel like someone is a problem or someone thinks you have a problem. Make a list of 10. Pick the least intense one to start, and use this relationship and situation to complete the second page of this worksheet.

1.

2.

3.

4.

5.

6.

7.

8.

9.

10.

How will I create belonging in spite of this problem so I continue to act like my relational self?

❑ Step one: I remember the relationship and name it.

❑ Step two: I quiet myself.

❑ Step three: I get my relational circuits on.

❑ Step four: I remember three ways I value this relationship and am glad to be in it.

❑ Step five: I look for signs that I need some healing – what emotions won't quiet?

❑ Step six: I get more Godsight by asking God to show me more in this relationship.

❑ Step seven: I create belonging by telling who we are together in this relationship and how we want this to end.

❑ I go slow – I go slower – I go even slower - because training takes time.

(Complete worksheet on the second page for the least intense problem.)

Part 2: Learning to make my relationship bigger than the problem.

Here is my problem with someone important to me:

How will I create belonging in spite of this problem so I continue to act like my relational self?

- ❑ Step one: I remember the relationship and name it.

- ❑ Step two: I quiet myself
    - ❑ Shalom my Body
    - ❑ Other things that help me quiet myself.

- ❑ Step three: I get my relational circuits on.
    - ❑ Shalom my Soul
    - ❑ Shalom for my Heart
    - ❑ Grow my appreciation

- ❑ Step four: I remember three ways I value this relationship and am glad to be in it.
    - ❑ 1.

    - ❑ 2.

    - ❑ 3.

- ❑ Step five: I look for signs that I need some healing – what emotions won't quiet?
    - ❑ Anger
    - ❑ Fear
    - ❑ Shame
    - ❑ Disgust
    - ❑ Hopeless/despair
    - ❑ Sadness

- ❑ Step six: I get more Godsight by asking God to show me more in this relationship.

- ❑ Step seven: I create belonging by telling *who we are together in this relationship*, and *how we want this to end.*

- ❑ I go slow – I go slower – I go even slower - because training takes time.

Coordinators: Random Acts of Creating Belonging Worksheet

©Copyright E. James Wilder Ph.D. and Ed Khouri, 2009.

Instructions:
This week, your Round Table members will be trying out their own style of creating belonging by making plans to express "random acts of creating belonging" around them at church. Use this form to list everyone's "random acts" goal.

This week, email this list to other Belonging Coordinators and to the members of your own Round Table.

Name	Random act of creating belonging goal

Go Shalom, Appreciation and RC Watching

A five-day log of observations about shalom, appreciation and my relational circuits
© Copyright E. James Wilder Ph.D. and Ed Khouri, 2009.

Instructions:
Each day, use this form to keep track of shalom, appreciation and your RCs. Briefly describe when you noticed that shalom, appreciation and your RCs were fading, and how the problem began. Next, place a check next to every statement that describes what happened when you lost shalom, appreciation and your RCs, and then place a check next to each step you used to restore them. Finally, write one word that best describes what it felt like emotionally and in your body when you lost shalom, appreciation and your RCs – and when they were restored.

Day 1: When did I notice that my shalom, appreciation and RCs faded? What started these fading?

What happened when I lost shalom, appreciation and my RCs?		
___ Attachment pain was involved.		___ My cravings increased.
___ I lost Godsight.		___ I stopped creating Belonging.
Which of the following steps did I use to restore shalom, appreciation and my RCs?		
___ RC Checklist	___ Shalom for my Body	___ Shalom for my Soul & Heart
The emotion validated was _____		The comfort was _____
When my shalom, appreciation and RCs faded:		**When shalom, appreciation & RCs were restored:**
The emotion I felt was _____		The emotion I felt was _____
My body felt _____		My body felt _____

Day 2: When did I notice that my shalom, appreciation and RCs faded? What started these fading?

What happened when I lost shalom, appreciation and my RCs?		
___ Attachment pain was involved.		___ My cravings increased.
___ I lost Godsight.		___ I stopped creating Belonging.
Which of the following steps did I use to restore shalom, appreciation and my RCs?		
___ RC Checklist	___ Shalom for my Body	___ Shalom for my Soul & Heart
The emotion validated was _____		The comfort was _____
When my shalom, appreciation and RCs faded:		**When shalom, appreciation & RCs were restored:**
The emotion I felt was _____		The emotion I felt was _____
My body felt _____		My body felt _____

Day 3: When did I notice that my shalom, appreciation and RCs faded? What started these fading?

What happened when I lost shalom, appreciation and my RCs?	
____ Attachment pain was involved.	____ My cravings increased.
____ I lost Godsight.	____ I stopped creating Belonging.
Which of the following steps did I use to restore shalom, appreciation and my RCs?	
____ RC Checklist ____ Shalom for my Body ____ Shalom for my Soul & Heart	
The emotion validated was _____	The comfort was _____
When my shalom, appreciation and RCs faded:	**When shalom, appreciation & RCs were restored:**
The emotion I felt was _____	The emotion I felt was _____
My body felt _____	My body felt _____

Day 4: When did I notice that my shalom, appreciation and RCs faded? What started these fading?

What happened when I lost shalom, appreciation and my RCs?	
____ Attachment pain was involved.	____ My cravings increased.
____ I lost Godsight.	____ I stopped creating Belonging.
Which of the following steps did I use to restore shalom, appreciation and my RCs?	
____ RC Checklist ____ Shalom for my Body ____ Shalom for my Soul & Heart	
The emotion validated was _____	The comfort was _____
When my shalom, appreciation and RCs faded:	**When shalom, appreciation & RCs were restored:**
The emotion I felt was _____	The emotion I felt was _____
My body felt _____	My body felt _____

Day 5: When did I notice that my shalom, appreciation and RCs faded? What started these fading?

What happened when I lost shalom, appreciation and my RCs?	
____ Attachment pain was involved.	____ My cravings increased.
____ I lost Godsight.	____ I stopped creating Belonging.
Which of the following steps did I use to restore shalom, appreciation and my RCs?	
____ RC Checklist ____ Shalom for my Body ____ Shalom for my Soul & Heart	
The emotion validated was _____	The comfort was _____
When my shalom, appreciation and RCs faded:	**When shalom, appreciation & RCs were restored:**
The emotion I felt was _____	The emotion I felt was _____
My body felt _____	My body felt _____

Notes

Chapter 7: Questions for Further Discussion

1. Imagine that you were present in the story of Jesus and the woman at the well. Which of the following characters in this story do you most closely identify with? Why? What do you think each of these might have been feeling?
   a. Jesus.
   b. The woman.
   c. The disciples.
   d. The people from the Samaritan village.

2. How did Godsight change the woman's identity - and the entire Samaritan Village? How do you think Godsight could change your relationship with God and how you see yourself? After answering these questions, make a list of at least 5 relationships that are important to you, and describe how Godsight could change these relationships. How have you seen these relationships over time, and how could Godsight change them now? Be specific!

3. Did you complete your Shalom Watching Worksheet this week? Did you notice attachment pain when your RCs began to fade? Describe what you did to help restore shalom, appreciation and your RCs. Were you able to return to shalom and appreciation with improvement in your RCs?

4. How does Jesus make His relationship with us bigger and more important than our problems? Is there anything we need to do to cooperate with Him? What does God do when we respond to Him?

5. What kind of things become possible when we see ourselves, God and others with Godsight when we are in the midst of a conflict? Think about at least one relationship in which you are experiencing conflict. What specific aspects of the conflict do you think you could better resolve if you viewed the situation with Godsight?

6. Describe the 5-bar moment or appreciation memory that you remembered during the Godsight exercise in class today. What emotions did you feel, and what did your body feel like? What did it feel like to reflect on this experience?

7. When you asked Jesus, "How do you see me right now?" what happened? What thoughts, impressions or feelings came to mind? How do these feel to you right now?

8. When you asked, "What style of belonging did you put in me?" what happened? What thoughts, impressions or feelings came to mind? How do these feel to you right now? Have you ever noticed these belonging styles in yourself? How could you begin to apply these?

9. What did you learn about telling Godsight stories to create belonging? How can you tell a Godsight story to create belonging, and how could you tell one that would keep others from wanting to belong? Right now, share a Godsight story with someone in your group! Remember to share what happened, and describe the emotions and body sensations you felt.

Notes

Notes

Belonging Chapter 8:

CRAVINGS, WILLPOWER AND "WHAT MAKES YOU BEHAVE YOURSELF?"

Group Opens:
• Ask a volunteer to open the group with prayer.

Belonging exercise: Random acts of creating belonging
This exercise has 2 parts. Part 1 is 15 minutes, and Part 2 is 5 minutes. Your facilitator will keep track of time for you.

Part 1:

1. Form groups of 3 from your Round Table to share your experiences with "random acts of creating belonging" at church this week.

2. As you share, answer these questions and express appreciation to group members for experimenting with their style of creating belonging at church this week!
   a. What did my "random act of creating belonging around me" feel like?
   b. What would I like to change next time?
   c. What would I like to do the same?

3. You will have 15 minutes for this part of the exercise.

Part 2:

1. You can remain in your small groups as your facilitator leads a class discussion to answer this question: What did my "random act of creating belonging around me" feel like?

2. Please share your answers to this question using one word only.

3. You will have 5 minutes for this part of the exercise.

Please start the Belonging DVD for this week's lesson.

Belonging Teaching: What makes you behave yourself? When cravings replace belonging

What does "Belonging" look like?
• Belonging is the joy we create around us!

Belonging is Training!

Weekly Bible Story: When cravings get your goats: The story of Esau and Jacob.

GOD'S PEACE, APPRECIATION AND JOYFUL BELONGING:
These are what my brain's relational circuits really crave!

Notes

We are created for a relational world where we live in shalom.
- Everything is in the right relationship,
- At the right strength and amount,
- In the right place,
- For God and people.
- Our relational circuits are on and we create belonging around us.

This is how we want to live.
- God's peace, appreciation and joyful belonging are what my brain's relational circuits really crave!

Attachment pain
- The kind of pain I feel when I've lost appreciation and shalom, and my RCs fade, is called attachment pain.
- We feel it, but may not recognize, understand or know what we are feeling.
- It is one of the main reasons our RCs shut down.

Attachment pain is the kind of distress I feel when:
- I don't feel connected to anyone.
- A person that I have been connected to is no longer present.
- There is distance between me and someone I've been connected with.
- I don't know where I belong nor have someone to belong to.

Attachment pain
- Can affect relationships with both God and others.
- Is sub-cortical – below conscious awareness.
- Is not observed or controlled by conscious thought.

Attachment pain is distress at Level 1 of the brain's control center.
- It is the deepest level of pain.

Intensity
- Attachment pain is so intense, that everything in us tries to make the pain go away by any means necessary.
- Attachment pain can pervade and affect every area of life.
- Everything hurts and feels more intense!

Craving Relief
- We soon find ourselves craving relief from our distress.
- But because our RCs are down, we can't engage with others to enjoy the connections we crave.

Cravings
- Attachment pain is often felt in the form of cravings.
- Because we all experience attachment pain and problems with our RCs, we all experience cravings!

EVERYONE EXPERIENCES CRAVINGS.
Since we all experience RC distress and attachment pain from time-to-time, we also tend to crave relief from our distress and pain. The only real differences are the degree of attachment pain, the intensity of our cravings - and the types of things we crave.

- We tend to crave the things we think will just make us feel less distress – or something to make us feel better.
- When our RCs are off, we don't realize that what we are really craving is joyful belonging!

While our individual cravings may all be different, they have one common theme:
- They all mask attachment pain and provide temporary relief from distress.

Cravings can become monsters when our RCs are off, no matter what we are craving!

When we feed our cravings long enough, they eventually become a source of attachment pain when we can't find the things we crave!

Cravings
- Living with ongoing attachment pain and our relational circuits turned off makes us very vulnerable to cravings and to the development of strong attachments to BEEPS.

BEEPS:
- Behaviors
- Events
- Experiences
- People
- Substances

How do you handle your cravings?
- What makes you "behave yourself?"

How long can you hold on – and keep your cravings fenced in?
- What happens when the cravings – and the distress – get stronger?

How do you manage that "other part of you" when you are craving?
- And what do you do with the pain?

How close can you get to the falls before it's too late?

Is willpower enough to make it all stop?

Unfortunately,
- Strategies emphasizing "knowing the right thing to do" and the use of willpower to control attachment pain, cravings and BEEPS sound good, but are doomed to fail.
- These strategies fail when we struggle with attachment pain, cravings & BEEPS, because they actually work against God's design for the brain.

Bad news for my brain:
- The brain is primarily relational, so any strategies that bypass the dominant relational and emotional centers of the brain to emphasize information and will as the means to handle cravings and BEEPS are not "Good News" at all.

> **INTELLECT AND WILLPOWER ARE NOT ENOUGH TO HANDLE CRAVINGS.**
> *Any attempts to handle attachment pain and cravings that rely primarily on "knowing the right thing to do" and the exercise of willpower are doomed to fail. These non-relational strategies actually work against God's design for the brain.*

Notes

Bad news for my brain and spirit:
- A good example of the "bad news for my brain and spirit" that has permeated Western Culture and Christianity for centuries is found in the writings of the Puritan, William Ames.
- "...It must be that the first beginning of faith lies in the will." (Faith & Preparation, William Ames).[1]
- Emphasizing the use of willpower as the basis of faith, life, spiritual growth and maturity – as well as the means of controlling attachment pain, cravings and BEEPS – creates a non-relational faith that rests on a foundation of human intellect, strength and effort and not on a loving, relational God.

Perhaps this helps explain the growing epidemics of addiction, trauma & trauma-based behaviors that are spreading rapidly across the globe.

Equipped with the wrong strategy to succeed, people fail.
- They are then ostracized, blamed, shamed and shunned for their "moral weakness," bad choices and failure.
- It never dawns on anyone that they have simply relied on the strategies they learned at church and in our culture.

But, what if we could learn to give our brain what it really needs – and learn to quiet our distress before our cravings become too strong?

Remember:
- Cravings come in all different kinds of forms and strengths – and are felt differently by everyone.
- We often crave more than one thing for relief.

By quieting our distress, the intensity of our cravings also decreases.

Quieting also restores shalom, helps us find appreciation, and re-activates our brain's RCs.

Affirmation is vital for quieting.
- Affirmation is the process of receiving validation and comfort to help us quiet and restore shalom, appreciation and our RCs.
- Affirmation allows us to connect with what our brain and spirit are really craving: joyful, life-giving relationships with God and others.

Learning to notice and quiet our attachment pain, cravings and BEEPS are essential Belonging skills.
- Here are four worksheets and exercises to help you get started!

The "Cravings and BEEPS Signs of Attachment Pain" checklists:
- Help us learn to recognize distress and cravings before they are out of control.

---

1 See Dr. Ames Essay, "Faith and Preparation" as reproduced on the website "A Puritan's Mind,"
http://www.apuritansmind.com/William%20Ames/WilliamAmesFaithPreparation.htm.

QUIETING HELPS REDUCE THE INTENSITY OF OUR CRAVINGS.

Our Cravings Worksheets and Belonging Quieting Steps help us return to shalom and appreciation with active RCs. This allows us to reconnect with God and others, helps restore joyful belonging, and reduces the intensity of cravings fueled by attachment pain. By giving our brain what it really needs, we decrease our cravings for BEEPS.

Notes

The "Do I Have a Craving?" Worksheet and exercise:
• Help us better understand and identify cravings, and recognize how they affect us.

The "Shalom for my Cravings" exercise and worksheet:
• Helps us quiet our cravings and return to shalom and appreciation with our RCs active.

Let's try the Cravings Signs of Attachment Pain Checklist.
• Find your checklist, pages 120-121, and get ready to spot your cravings.

As you begin, here are a few "Wise Thoughts about Cravings" for you to consider.
• Wise Thought Number 1:
  o Since we all experience RC impairment and attachment pain, we all have cravings.
• Wise Thought Number 2:
  o Some cravings are more intense than others and can include a wide range of things.
• Wise Thought Number 3:
  o The longer we experience cravings, the more likely we are to give into them.
• Wise Thought Number 4:
  o By learning to recognize cravings and restore our RCs, we can give our brain what it really wants – joy, relationship and belonging.

We can become relational again, live in shalom with appreciation and create belonging around us! Have fun with your checklist!

Belonging Exercise: My Cravings Checklist
Your facilitator will lead you through this 10 minute exercise.

1. You can remain at your Round Table for this 10 minute exercise.

2. Your facilitator will go through the Cravings Signs for Attachment Pain Checklist, pages 120-121, with the entire Belonging class, and help you learn to complete it.

3. As your facilitator leads you through the checklist, please mark each statement that applies to you.

4. Please complete the BEEPS Signs of Attachment Pain portion of the checklist, pages 122-124, at home.
   a. You do not have to do this in class.
   b. You can be known but your BEEPS can remain anonymous!

5. When everyone has completed the checklist, your facilitator will lead you through an RC check and the Shalom for my Body Exercise.

Belonging exercise: RC Check and Shalom for my Body
You will have 1 minute for a quick RC Check using your short form, and 4 minutes for the Shalom for my Body exercise.

1. Please remain at your Round Table as your facilitator leads the class through an RC Check and Shalom for my Body exercise.

> ### THIS WEEK, WE'LL LEARN THESE BELONGING TOOLS FOR CRAVINGS:
> *The Cravings and BEEPS Signs of Attachment Pain Checklist.*
> *The "Do I Have A Craving?" Worksheet.*
> *The Shalom for my Cravings Exercise.*
> *The Track My Cravings Log.*

Notes

2. Check your RCs using the Shalom for my Body Short Form
   - ❑ I just want to make a problem, person or feeling go away.
   - ❑ I don't want to listen to what others feel or say.
   - ❑ My mind is "locked onto" something upsetting.
   - ❑ I don't want to be connected to? (someone I usually like)
   - ❑ I just want to get away, or fight or I freeze.
   - ❑ I more aggressively interrogate, judge and fix others.

3. When you have finished the RC Check, your facilitator will lead the class in the Shalom for my Body exercise.
   a. Set the timing right with the verse based on Psalm 56:3: "Whenever I am afraid I will trust in you O Lord."
   b. Move your body (4 moves).
   c. Breathe and scrunch.
   d. Yawn left and right.
   e. Knock to wake up your attachment center.
   f. Get the sympathetic and parasympathetic synchronized with each other (change speeds).

Belonging exercise: "Do I Have a Craving?" Worksheet
This is a 25 minute exercise, and your facilitator will keep track of time for you.

1. Please remain at your Round Table for this exercise, and follow your facilitator's instructions to complete and discuss your worksheet, page 125.

2. To complete your worksheet, write your answer to each question about cravings in the space provided.

3. Volunteers may share their answers to the worksheet questions with their Round Table, and may also ask their Round Table for help completing the worksheet.

4. Not everyone will have time to get help from the group.
   a. If you would like to ask your group to help you complete the worksheet, please ask.
   b. Please listen to the Round Table discussion, because some of your questions may be answered as your Round Table helps other members with their worksheets.

5. Important Note: Do not complete the "Take Home" section of the worksheet. This is for homework. In Belonging, your BEEPS can remain anonymous – while you are known and belong!

Belonging exercise: Shalom for my Cravings Worksheet
Your instructor will lead you through this 10 minute exercise.

Introduction

1. Please stay at your Round Table as your facilitator reviews the Shalom for my Cravings Worksheet with you, and helps you learn how to complete it. The worksheet is similar to your Shalom for my Soul and Heart Worksheet. The worksheet is on page 127.

> ### IMPORTANT NOTE ABOUT BELONGING, CRAVINGS AND BEEPS:
> *In Belonging, and in all of our Belonging in-class exercises, worksheets and discussions, we want you to be known and loved - and your BEEPS can remain anonymous.*

2. This worksheet is for homework only, and is not to be completed in class. Remember - You can be known, but your BEEPs can remain anonymous.

3. Please pay attention to these guidelines and to the instructions listed below.
   a. Honestly share your answers to each question, with all the feeling you can express, out loud to God.
   b. Use your attachment pain checklist and your cravings checklists to help you.
   c. Be sure to use the Shalom for my Body exercise to quiet your nervous system first.
   d. Rate the strength of your cravings before and after the exercise.
   e. When you have finished, be sure to follow through with anyone you need to connect with. This could be a friend, support person or group.

4. We will have 10 minutes to learn to use the worksheet, and to answer questions.

Shalom for my Cravings Instructions

1. To Start:
   a. Circle the number that best describes how strong your cravings are right now.
   b. Rate your cravings on a scale of 1 (lowest) to 10 (highest) before (and then after) completing this worksheet. Circle the number that best describes their intensity.

2. Be sure to complete the Shalom for my Body exercise before completing the rest of the worksheet.

3. Follow the questions and instructions in sections 1- 6 of the worksheet.
   a. Express your answers out loud to God with as much feeling as you need.
   b. It may be helpful to write your answers, and then read them out loud to God when you are finished.

4. Make sure you follow through and connect with anyone you listed in question 6.

5. Finally, rate your cravings again after you have completed the entire worksheet.

Belonging Homework: Week 8

Everyone:

Random acts of creating belonging.
- Try another "Random act of creating Belonging around me" at church, with improvements based on what you learned from last week's experience.

Monitor, track and quiet cravings this week.
- Complete your BEEPS Signs Of Attachment Pain worksheet, pages 122-124, at home.
- Complete your "Do I Have A Craving?" Worksheet, page 125, at home if you did not finish it in class.
- Use your Shalom My Cravings worksheet, page 127, this week when you discover a craving.
- Use the Track My Cravings log, pages 128-129, this week to monitor your cravings.

Optional Exercise: Go Shalom Watching, pages 130-131.
- Add "Cravings" to your list of observations of things that result in the loss of shalom and appreciation, and cause your RCs to fade.
- Then, use the steps you've learned so far to get your RCs back on!

Notes

Cravings Signs of Attachment Pain

Copyright E. James Wilder Ph.D. and Ed Khouri 2009.

Cravings are what we experience when the brain is longing for joyful connections with God and others, but can't have them because our relational connection circuits are offline. Cravings follow attachment pain, and are the brain's way of saying, "I need connections to someone - and I need them now!" The things we crave tend to be the things we desire to help turn off our attachment pain. Learning to recognize cravings as an expression of attachment pain can help us monitor our relational connection circuits - before our cravings become impossible to resist.

- ❏ I have physical signs of cravings:
    - ❏ I still feel hungry.
    - ❏ I still want more of that.
    - ❏ I still want something sweet.
    - ❏ I want to get that feeling back.
    - ❏ I just want to get rid of this feeling.
- ❏ I do things just to get attention.
- ❏ I make people laugh even when I don't feel happy.
- ❏ I start snacking on or eating my comfort foods. (Make a list of your personal favorites.)
- ❏ I feel "antsy" and bored and want to do something really exciting.
- ❏ I forget my priorities while looking for entertainment or pleasure.
- ❏ I don't keep my resolutions (like when I drop off my healthy eating diet).
- ❏ I am spending more time on the computer than with people when I'm not at work.
- ❏ I am spending more time on video games, shopping or watching shows than with people.
- ❏ I am spending increasing amounts of time thinking about how good life used to feel.
- ❏ I am spending an increasing amount of time trying to find or maintain relationships that I hope will make me feel better.
- ❏ I feel jealous of the good things and relationships that others have.
- ❏ I would feel better if I could have what my friends and the people around me have.
- ❏ I feel restless and am looking, scanning, "surfing," shopping, driving around, browsing or wandering.
- ❏ I repeatedly go back to the same thing (like email box, refrigerator, computer or TV) looking for something new.
- ❏ I play video games over and over.
- ❏ I am spending so much mental energy on work and projects that I do not have enough energy to spend with my family and with God.
- ❏ I am spending money impulsively.
- ❏ I need to feel better right now...even if I am not sure how.
- ❏ I feel like God is distant and nothing seems to help, even though I spend more time at church, reading my Bible, praying or spending time with other Christians.
- ❏ When I feel bad, I think of someone I can go and help.
- ❏ I work very hard not to make mistakes, and I feel ashamed when I fail.
- ❏ I feel much safer if I am the one in charge.

❑ When people are in spiritual error, it gets under my skin until I correct and instruct them.

❑ I find that I am spending more time thinking about using:

    ❑ Alcohol.

    ❑ Nicotine.

    ❑ More caffeine or energy drinks.

    ❑ Illegal drugs.

    ❑ More prescription medication than what is prescribed for me.

    ❑ Gambling.

    ❑ Sex.

    ❑ Comfort or other foods.

    ❑ Buying new things.

    ❑ Work or ministry needs.

BEEPS Signs Of Attachment Pain

What are BEEPS and how do they fit with cravings and attachment pain?

When our relational circuits are off and we are in attachment pain, our cravings grow until it feels like everything in us is crying out for relief. BEEPS are the Behaviors, Events, Experiences, People and Substances that we use to help ease attachment pain, handle negative emotions, increase pleasure or decrease pain. BEEPS activate the same regions of the brain that are normally used to experience and create belonging in genuine joyful relationships with God and others. BEEPS trigger the pleasure/reward centers of the brain in much the same way that joyful relationships do. By activating these relational circuits, BEEPS actually temporarily "turn off" attachment pain. The brain is tricked into building and creating belonging for itself around BEEPS – and not genuine joyful relationships with God and others. The "BEEPS Signs of Attachment Pain" checklist can help us recognize the signs of harmful connections with BEEPS. No matter how they began, BEEPS inevitably de-activate our relational connection circuitry and indicate the presence of attachment pain. By learning to skillfully use this checklist to monitor our use of BEEPS, we can:

1. Learn to recognize our use of BEEPS before they become catastrophic.
2. Identify our use of BEEPS as an indicator that our relational connection circuits are offline.
3. Recognize the signs of possible BEEPS relapse.
4. Recognize when BEEPS start producing their own attachment pain.
5. Use these warnings to restart my relational circuits by using Belonging skills.

Since we all experience our own unique attachment pain, we all also tend to have our own unique flavor of BEEPS to manage the pain. It is not important that your own personal BEEPS are known and shared with the Belonging group because your BEEPS are not the basis for your belonging. In Belonging, and in the entire Thriving: Recover Your Life program, we want you to be known through how God sees you and to learn to create belonging around you by seeing others the same way. Do not complete the remainder of this checklist as a part of a Belonging group activity. Don't share this with your Belonging group. This is for your personal use only.

Notes

BEEPS Signs Of Attachment Pain Checklist

Note: The presence of one or more of these indicators by themselves does not necessarily indicate the presence of significant attachment pain or BEEPS.

Complete this portion of the checklist at home.

- ❑ I make sure that I buy comfort foods when I shop.
- ❑ I keep track of my comfort food at home so that I am sure I don't run out.
- ❑ I am planning where I could get what I crave.
- ❑ My doctor has told me that I need to lose weight, but I can't stick to my diet.
- ❑ My weight is causing medical problems for me.
- ❑ My diabetes, heart disease or other medical condition is related to my diet, but I still find myself eating foods that make the problem worse.
- ❑ I keep thinking "I could use some _____" (my BEEPS).
- ❑ I am staying home from work when I am not sick.
- ❑ I have increased masturbation or sexual tension.
- ❑ My use of _____ is increasing.
    - ❑ Alcohol
    - ❑ Nicotine
    - ❑ Coffee, caffeine or energy drinks
    - ❑ Illegal drugs
    - ❑ More prescription medication than what is prescribed for me
    - ❑ Gambling
    - ❑ Sex
    - ❑ Sugar, comfort or other foods
    - ❑ Buying new things
    - ❑ Work
- ❑ I am spending more time missing the "good old days" and friends I used to have when I used BEEPS.
- ❑ I spend more time thinking about the places where I used BEEPS, even though I know I shouldn't go there.
- ❑ Even though I haven't used BEEPS, the amount of time I spend thinking about BEEPS has increased.
- ❑ I am starting to think that a little of my BEEPS, used in moderation, is not bad.
- ❑ I'm spending more time in the places where I used to use BEEPS.
- ❑ I am thinking about using BEEPS, even though I don't plan to use them.
- ❑ I have been remembering the high lately and thinking how my BEEPS make me feel.
- ❑ Though I'm not accessing hard core pornographic websites, I surf the net and click on questionable links in the hopes that I may find something that is sexually arousing.
- ❑ I find myself taking unnecessary physical risks doing dangerous activities because I can't stand to be bored.
- ❑ I am hoarding or hiding the "good stuff" from others.

❑ I am hiding some of my activities from those closest to me.

❑ I am using more prescription medication than is prescribed for me.

❑ I am visiting multiple doctors to obtain pain medications.

❑ I am asking others to share their medications with me.

❑ I am cruising the "red light district" in hopes of catching a glimpse of something exciting.

❑ I feel increasing urges to act out sexually in ways that could get me in trouble with my spouse, my partner or the law.

❑ After I eat, lately all I can think of is getting the food out of my system as quickly as possible.

❑ I am feeling very guilty and ashamed of my weight gain.

❑ I buy and use laxatives to avoid weight gain.

❑ I have been hanging out in places where I know that drugs are available.

❑ I am smoking more than I used to.

❑ People tell me that I am very controlling - but I disagree.

❑ I keep thinking how much better my life would be if people around me would just behave!

❑ When I am feeling upset, I think about others that I can minister to.

❑ If I am not helping others, I start to feel restless, irritable or sad.

❑ When I'm not at work, I spend most of my time:

    ❑ In front of the TV.

    ❑ In front of the computer.

    ❑ Playing fantasy role-playing games.

    ❑ Playing video games.

    ❑ Playing online poker.

❑ I am in debt because of gambling.

❑ I move from one very high intensity relationship to another with very little time between.

❑ Most of my relationships become sexual.

❑ Even though I don't always want to, I make excuses for the behavior of people around me that I love so they won't feel so bad.

❑ I am shouldering the duties of others, because their use of BEEPS makes it hard for them to carry their own responsibilities.

❑ I spend a lot of time worrying about how my spouse, partner or family member is hurting himself/herself with the use of drugs, alcohol, food or other BEEPS.

❑ I feel like my partner's use of BEEPS is destroying my life.

❑ My partner hits me, but I'm sure he/she doesn't mean it and still loves me.

❑ At times, I find it necessary to hit or physically grab my partner or children because they are not listening to me.

❑ I find that I am spending more time working because it's easier than the stress at home.

❑ I am discovering that it's easier for me to complete tasks at work than it is for me to relate to people around me at home or at work.

❑ I find that cutting or injuring myself isn't really all that bad.

Notes

Signs that I Have Attachment Pain Because I Can't Have my BEEPS:

❑ When I stop using my BEEPS, I get physically sick.

❑ When I stop using BEEPS, I feel increasingly depressed or anxious.

❑ Without BEEPS, I feel like I can't sleep or rest.

❑ I am contemplating elective surgeries that will require pain medication, even though I've had problems with misuse of pain medications before.

❑ My use of BEEPS might - or has already - gotten me in trouble with the law.

❑ I have lost a relationship that was important to me over my use of BEEPS.

❑ I have lost a relationship because of multiple sexual partners.

❑ Someone that was important to me has told me that I have a problem using BEEPS.

❑ I have been through an addiction treatment program, but I continue to do the same things that caused me to go into treatment.

❑ I am in danger of losing my job - or I've already lost a job - because of my use of BEEPS.

❑ I keep on feeling the intense need never to make a mistake.

❑ I can't imagine a week without BEEPS.

❑ My use of BEEPS has resulted in serious medical problems or symptoms:

    ❑ I can't remember what I did the night before while using BEEPS.

    ❑ Cirrhosis of the liver.

    ❑ Heart disease.

    ❑ Lung cancer.

    ❑ Diabetes.

    ❑ Problems with memory.

    ❑ Shaking, tremors or facial tics.

    ❑ DTs.

    ❑ HIV/AIDS.

    ❑ Sexually transmitted disease.

    ❑ Anxiety.

    ❑ Depression.

    ❑ Broken bones.

    ❑ Bleeding in my digestive tract.

    ❑ Jaundice.

    ❑ Malnutrition.

    ❑ Gangrene.

    ❑ Hepatitis.

    ❑ Loss of teeth.

Do I Have a Craving? Worksheet

Copyright E. James Wilder Ph.D. and Ed Khouri 2009.

What are the many things that I crave from time to time? List at least ten. *Do not discuss your answers.*
(Foods, drinks, sweets, distractions/entertainment/tv/movies, electronic/computer, buying/shopping, sensory, excitement, tobacco, work/school/success/control, people, rushes, highs and buzzes, chemicals, sexual and other.)

FOR ROUND TABLE DISCUSSION:

When do I most experience cravings?
(When there is a bothersome problem in my life, morning, evening, weekends, alone, at work, while driving, when tired, certain times of month, when it has been too long, when bored, after a fight, holidays and others.)

How do I usually handle my cravings?
(I don't notice and just do it, I fight the urge, I start my rituals to prepare, I begin the search, it depends on what I crave, such as...)

What are my relational circuits doing when I crave? (Go Shalom Watching)
(Usually off, fading, flooded by emotion, filled with attachment pain, forgotten or other)

When do I notice that my relational circuits are off?
 (Not until much later, not at all, at Belonging class, the next day, that night or other)

When do my relational circuits come back on?
(On their own some time, overnight, when I do the Belonging steps, with prayer or other.)

When problems become bigger than my relationships, do my cravings get stronger or more frequent?

TAKE HOME SECTION: *Do not discuss the following section or your answers in class.*

What BEEPS do I want to use? (Take the take home cravings checklist.)

What is it that I really need?

Notes

Shalom for My Cravings Worksheet

Introduction

We are designed so that our spirit, mind, brain and body function best when living in shalom. In shalom, we are able to create belonging around us, and experience joyful relationships with God and with others. Shalom is a Hebrew word that describes what it is like when everything is in the right relationship, at the right time, in the right place, at the right strength and in the right amount for God and people. When we are in shalom, our relational circuits are on. As a result, we are able to respond constructively to attachment pain and control our cravings.

When we are not in shalom and our relational connection circuits are not working well, we experience attachment pain. Attachment pain is the distress we feel when connections to God and others who are important to us are disrupted. This pain is so deep that it exists below a level of consciousness, but it tends to affect every part of us: body, mind, brain and spirit. When our body, mind, brain or spirit are in distress, it is not long before that pain is expressed by cravings for something or someone to help make the hurt feel better. When we are not good at keeping track of our relational circuits or recognizing attachment pain, our cravings can often give us the first clue that we are not in shalom. Recognizing the feelings and body sensations that can accompany cravings can be an important first step in the process of returning to shalom.

Sometimes the feelings that accompany cravings are subtle. Cravings can feel like a small itch that can't be easily scratched, a vague feeling of discontent, irritability, a nagging sense that we need something or someone to "pick us up," or the restlessness that leads to wandering. As cravings become more intense, they can feel as powerful as a restless lion pacing back and forth at the zoo. Cravings can feel like the roar in our head pushing us towards the person or thing we desire, the screaming inside for relief, the sense of hopeless desperation that drives us to feel better at any cost – or even the sense of anticipation and excitement about the good feelings we'll get if we just go ahead and do what we feel like doing. These are only a few examples of the feelings that often accompany our cravings.

Our bodies can also help us recognize cravings. We may feel butterflies in our stomach when we anticipate the excitement of getting what we want. Heads pound, hearts race, and we may feel hungry for something…even though we have just finished a meal. Tapping feet, a restless pacing, nervous energy and the inability to turn off the anxiety keep us in a constant state of arousal. Tears, exhaustion and feeling that we just can't get moving leave us hungry for something to get us through the day. Sometimes, we physically shake or remember how good it felt the last time we gave into our cravings, making it hard to think of anything else.

The longer these feelings and sensations continue, the more likely we are to give into them. That's why it's important both to recognize our cravings – and to re-activate our relational circuits so that we can return to shalom. With our relational circuits working, we are able to connect to God and to others – which is what our brain, mind, body and spirit need. When our relational connection circuits are working from shalom, we discover that the intensity of our cravings are reduced, and find the relational resources we need to overcome them.

Quieting: Shalom for my Cravings

©*Copyright E. James Wilder Ph.D. and Ed Khouri, 2009.*

Our goal: Quiet our cravings when we experience attachment pain so we can return to shalom and appreciation with our relational circuits restored.

Instructions: Honestly share your answers to each question, with all the feeling you can express, out loud with God. Use your attachment pain checklist and cravings checklists to help you. It is a good idea to practice Shalom for my Body first. Rate the strength of your cravings before and after this exercise. When you have finished, see if you can remember any promises God has made you.

Circle the number that best describes how strong your cravings are now. (Lowest) 1 – 2 – 3 – 4 – 5 – 6 – 7 – 8 – 9 – 10 (Highest).

☐ I have done my Shalom for my Body exercise.

1.	What does my attachment pain feel like right now and what am I craving? *Use your attachment pain checklist and cravings checklist to help if you have trouble answering.*
2.	What does it feel like I am missing from relationship right now? Keep telling God about your attachment pain, cravings and what you feel like you need from relationship until you are also able to tell God how your body feels right now. After 5 minutes, if you are still feeling strong attachment pain and cravings, focus on any part of your situation that is sad. Tell God how you and others hurt in this situation, and how your body feels now. Is there any part of this situation that makes God sad?
3.	Ask God to show you where He sees you were hurt and what you need most from relationships now. (Sometimes this is a repeating injury and brings up other hurts.)
4.	What is different about this situation now that God and I are looking at things together?
5.	What do I appreciate or long for when God joins me? Share your appreciation with God, and tell Him what your longing feels like.
6.	Is there someone I need to connect with now? This could be a friend, support person or group.

Circle the number that best describes how strong your cravings are now. (Lowest) 1 – 2 – 3 – 4 – 5 – 6 – 7 – 8 – 9 – 10 (Highest).

Are there any promises I can remember that God has made to me? List them below.

Notes

Track my Cravings Log
Copyright E. James Wilder Ph.D. and Ed Khouri 2009.

Instructions:

To complete this worksheet, be sure you finish the entire Cravings Signs for Attachment Pain Checklist. We covered the first part of the worksheet in class, and you should complete the "BEEPS Signs of Attachment Pain" portion of the checklist at home. When you are finished, use this worksheet to keep a log of your cravings and BEEPS this week. You do not have to share this log or worksheet with anyone.

Day 1: What cravings am I having, or what BEEPS do I want to use?

What is it that I really need?

Tracking my cravings today:
  A. What am I feeling?

  B. What do I want?

  C. What do I do? (habits, rituals and BEEPS)

  D. How do I get my relational circuits back online?

Day 2: What cravings am I having, or what BEEPS do I want to use?

What is it that I really need?

Tracking my cravings today:
  A. What am I feeling?

  B. What do I want?

  C. What do I do? (habits, rituals and BEEPS)

  D. How do I get my relational circuits back online?

Day 3: What cravings am I having, or what BEEPS do I want to use?

What is it that I really need?

Tracking my cravings today:
  A. What am I feeling?

  B. What do I want?

  C. What do I do? (habits, rituals and BEEPS)

  D. How do I get my relational circuits back online?

Day 4: What cravings am I having, or what BEEPS do I want to use?

What is it that I really need?

Tracking my cravings today:
  A. What am I feeling?

  B. What do I want?

  C. What do I do? (habits, rituals and BEEPS)

  D. How do I get my relational circuits back online?

Day 5: What cravings am I having, or what BEEPS do I want to use?

What is it that I really need?

Tracking my cravings today:
  A. What am I feeling?

  B. What do I want?

  C. What do I do? (habits, rituals and BEEPS)

  D. How do I get my relational circuits back online?

Go Shalom, Appreciation And RC Watching

A five-day log of observations about shalom, appreciation and my relational circuits
© Copyright E. James Wilder Ph.D. and Ed Khouri, 2009.

Instructions:

Each day, use this form to keep track of shalom, appreciation and your RCs. Briefly describe when you noticed that shalom, appreciation and your RCs were fading, and how the problem began. Next, place a check next to every statement that describes what happened when you lost shalom, appreciation and your RCs, then place a check next to each step you used to restore them. Finally, write one word that best describes what it felt like emotionally and in your body when you lost shalom, appreciation and your RCs – and when they were restored.

Day 1: When did I notice that my shalom, appreciation and RCs faded? What started these fading?

What happened when I lost shalom, appreciation and my RCs?		
____ Attachment pain was involved.	____ My cravings increased.	
____ I lost Godsight.	____ I stopped creating Belonging.	
Which of the following steps did I use to restore shalom, appreciation and my RCs?		
____ RC Checklist	____ Shalom for my Body	____ Shalom for my Soul & Heart
The emotion validated was _____	The comfort was _____	
When my shalom, appreciation and RCs faded:	**When shalom, appreciation & RCs were restored:**	
The emotion I felt was _____	The emotion I felt was _____	
My body felt _____	My body felt _____	

Day 2: When did I notice that my shalom, appreciation and RCs faded? What started these fading?

What happened when I lost shalom, appreciation and my RCs?		
____ Attachment pain was involved.	____ My cravings increased.	
____ I lost Godsight.	____ I stopped creating Belonging.	
Which of the following steps did I use to restore shalom, appreciation and my RCs?		
____ RC Checklist	____ Shalom for my Body	____ Shalom for my Soul & Heart
The emotion validated was _____	The comfort was _____	
When my shalom, appreciation and RCs faded:	**When shalom, appreciation & RCs were restored:**	
The emotion I felt was _____	The emotion I felt was _____	
My body felt _____	My body felt _____	

Day 3: When did I notice that my shalom, appreciation and RCs faded? What started these fading?

What happened when I lost shalom, appreciation and my RCs?			
___ Attachment pain was involved.		___ My cravings increased.	
___ I lost Godsight.		___ I stopped creating Belonging.	
Which of the following steps did I use to restore shalom, appreciation and my RCs?			
___ RC Checklist	___ Shalom for my Body		___ Shalom for my Soul & Heart
The emotion validated was _____		The comfort was _____	
When my shalom, appreciation and RCs faded:		**When shalom, appreciation & RCs were restored:**	
The emotion I felt was _____		The emotion I felt was _____	
My body felt _____		My body felt _____	

Day 4: When did I notice that my shalom, appreciation and RCs faded? What started these fading?

What happened when I lost shalom, appreciation and my RCs?			
___ Attachment pain was involved.		___ My cravings increased.	
___ I lost Godsight.		___ I stopped creating Belonging.	
Which of the following steps did I use to restore shalom, appreciation and my RCs?			
___ RC Checklist	___ Shalom for my Body		___ Shalom for my Soul & Heart
The emotion validated was _____		The comfort was _____	
When my shalom, appreciation and RCs faded:		**When shalom, appreciation & RCs were restored:**	
The emotion I felt was _____		The emotion I felt was _____	
My body felt _____		My body felt _____	

Day 5: When did I notice that my shalom, appreciation and RCs faded? What started these fading?

What happened when I lost shalom, appreciation and my RCs?			
___ Attachment pain was involved.		___ My cravings increased.	
___ I lost Godsight.		___ I stopped creating Belonging.	
Which of the following steps did I use to restore shalom, appreciation and my RCs?			
___ RC Checklist	___ Shalom for my Body		___ Shalom for my Soul & Heart
The emotion validated was _____		The comfort was _____	
When my shalom, appreciation and RCs faded:		**When shalom, appreciation & RCs were restored:**	
The emotion I felt was _____		The emotion I felt was _____	
My body felt _____		My body felt _____	

Notes

Chapter 8: Questions for Further Discussion

1. This week, you practiced a "random act of creating belonging" at church. What did that random act of creating belonging feel like to you? What did you learn about your own style of creating belonging?

2. This week's Bible story was about Jacob, Esau and cravings. Are there times when you acted more like Jacob and took advantage of someone who was experiencing intense cravings? Are there times when you acted more like Esau, and lost things that were valuable because of intense cravings? List at least 2 of these experiences. Describe what happened, what you lost and what happened to your relationship. What was happening with your RCs at the time? How might these situations have been different if your RCs had been fully active?

3. Why do all of us experience cravings, and why can cravings become such monsters when we lose shalom, appreciation and our RCs?

4. What are BEEPS and why do we become attached to BEEPS?

5. In the past, what kind of strategies have you used to try and handle your cravings? How successful have you been when you've tried to handle attachment pain and cravings through willpower alone? Has willpower ever been enough to "make you behave?" Describe at least one experience when you tried to use willpower to make yourself "behave." What happened? Be as specific as you can be.

6. What signs of cravings did you notice when you completed the Cravings Signs of Attachment Pain Checklist? Please note the following as you answer this question:
   a. If you are completing these questions as part of an open Belonging Group, please only share your responses from the Cravings Signs of Attachment Pain Checklist - and not the BEEPS portion of the checklist you completed at home.
   b. If you are completing these questions as part of a program that is specifically addressing addictions, you may include the BEEPS Signs of Attachment Pain in your responses to this question.

7. From your Do I Have a Craving? Worksheet that you completed in class, please share your answers to the following questions:
   a. When do I most experience cravings?
   b. How do I usually handle my cravings?
   c. What are my RCs doing when I crave?
   d. When do I notice that my RCs are off?
   e. When do my RCs come back on?
   f. When problems become bigger than relationships, do my cravings get stronger or more frequent?
   g. Additional question: What happens to my desire and ability to create belonging when I am craving?

8. Did you practice your Shalom for my Cravings Worksheet this week? How strong were your cravings when you started the worksheet, and how strong were they when you were finished? Were you able to return to shalom and appreciation with your RCs active? Are there people or groups you need to contact when your cravings are very intense? Who are these people or groups, and how will you contact them?

Notes

9. What did you learn about your cravings from the Track My Cravings Log this week? Use the log to answer the following questions about your cravings from one day this past week:
    a. What cravings am I having or what BEEPS do I want to use?
    b. What is it that I really need?
    c. What am I feeling?
    d. What do I want?
    e. What do I do? (habits, rituals and BEEPS)
    f. How do I get my relational circuits back online?

Notes

Belonging Chapter 9:

KNOWING WHEN TO STOP!

Group Opens:
• Ask a volunteer to open the group with prayer.

Belonging exercise: Random Acts of Creating Belonging
This is a 15 minute exercise, and your facilitator will keep track of time for you.

1. Form groups of 3 from your Round Table as you share your experiences with your "random acts of creating belonging" at church this week.

2. To help you share, answer the following questions and express appreciation to your group members for experimenting with their style of creating belonging at church this week.
   a. Did your "random act of creating belonging" feel different to you this time?
   b. What have you learned about your style of creating belonging?

3. Your facilitator will let you know when it is time to start the next exercise.

Belonging Exercise: Shalom & Cravings Watching Report
This is a 15 minute exercise, and your facilitator will keep track of time for you.

1. Please remain in groups of 3 from your Round Table for this exercise.

2. Follow your facilitator's instructions, and share your experiences with "Shalom and Cravings Watching" from the past week.   The following questions can help guide you:
   a. How did you do with shalom, appreciation, RCs, attachment pain and cravings this week?
   b. Did anyone notice cravings or attachment pain this week?
   c. Did anyone return to shalom and appreciation with RCs active using our Belonging quieting steps?
   d. How did you quiet?
   e. Were you able to recognize the validation and comfort you received?
   f. What did your emotions and body feel like before and after you quieted and returned to shalom and appreciation with RCs active?

3. You can use any of the worksheets from last week's class and homework to help you share your shalom and craving experiences and insights:
   a. Track my Cravings Log
   b. Do I Have a Craving?
   c. Shalom for my Cravings
   d. Go Shalom Watching

4. Please remember these 2 important points as you share:
   a. Don't overwhelm each other with intensity as you share. It is helpful to share stories that are mild to moderate in intensity.   Sharing stories about cravings and distress that are intense may be overwhelming to others and may cause their RCs to shut down.
   b. Remember: You can be known and loved in Belonging, and your BEEPS can remain anonymous.

Notes

Belonging Teaching Note: Introducing Tracks 1 and 2

This week's lesson has two separate teaching and exercise tracks to help you learn and practice important new belonging skills. The first track is "Discovering my own unique gifts and style for creating Belonging." The second track is called "Knowing when to stop." Let's get started with Track 1.

Please start the Belonging DVD for this week's lesson.

Belonging Teaching Track 1: Discovering my own unique gifts and style for creating Belonging.

What does "Belonging" look like?
• Belonging is the joy we create around us!

Belonging is Training!

Weekly Bible Story: "Hey Moses, what's that in your hand?"
• Discovering my own unique gifts and style for creating Belonging

How do you like to create belonging? What's that in your hands right now?
• What about someone who likes to cook? How do you think someone who likes to cook can create belonging?
• What about someone who enjoys music? How could a love of music help someone create belonging?
• What about someone who likes sports? How could he or she create belonging?
• What about a medical professional? How could a medical professional create belonging?

What about the characteristics of your heart? Could they help you create belonging?
• Suppose you are tender-hearted? Could this help you create belonging?
• What about compassion? Can compassion help create belonging?
• Or, how about a heart full of joy? Can joy help create belonging?

Can we learn anything about how we create belonging from TV shows, books and movies?
• Is there a time you saw belonging created well on TV or in a book or movie?
• What resonated in you?
• Does this have anything to say about how you like to create belonging?

Prepare to stop the DVD for a short Belonging exercise:
• Take 2 minutes and tell the person next to you what your favorite TV, movie or book character's style for creating belonging looks like!
• When you finish sharing: Your facilitator will guide you through a series of "Belonging Improv." exercises to help you practice your own unique style of creating belonging.

WHAT IS YOUR OWN PERSONAL BELONGING STYLE?
God has given us each unique talents, gifts and abilities to create belonging that reflect aspects of God's character and nature. Discovering and developing our own personal style of creating belonging feels life-giving, affirming and nurturing to us and to others.

Pause the DVD for a series of Belonging exercises.
When you have completed all of the "Belonging Improv." exercises, in this track, please restart the DVD for the second teaching and exercise track, "Knowing when to stop."

Belonging Exercise: My favorite TV, book, or movie character's style of creating belonging.

This is a 2 minute exercise, and your facilitator will keep track of time for you.

1. Please remain at your Round Table for this class exercise.

2. Take 2 minutes and tell the person next to you what your favorite TV, movie or book character's style for creating belonging looks like!

3. Your facilitator will let you know when it is time to begin the next exercise.

Belonging Exercise: Belonging Improvisation 1.

This is a 10 minute exercise, and your facilitator will keep track of time for you.

1. Please form small groups of 3 with other members of your Round Table.

2. Once your groups have formed, take 10 minutes to do something right now to create belonging around you with members of your group.

3. Here are a few activity suggestions to help you:
   a. Use your own style of creating belonging!
   b. Smile and be interested in what others say.
   c. Ask if they had answers to prayer from last week.
   d. Tell them something you have learned about your style of creating belonging and ask about theirs.
   e. Tell them your 5 bar moment – and ask about theirs.
   f. Tell them how Jesus saw you, and ask how Jesus saw them.
   g. Tell them a mini-appreciation story.

4. Your facilitator will keep track of time for you, and let you know when it is time for Belonging Improv. Exercise 2.

Belonging Exercise: Belonging Improvisation 2: Tell stories that turn on relational circuits and create belonging.

This is an 8 minute exercise, and your facilitator will keep track of time for you.

1. For this exercise, you do not have to remain at your Round Table.

2. Find someone in class you do not know well, and tell an appreciation story about something you have seen done to create belonging here in class.

3. Neither you nor the person you share the appreciation story with need to be the one who did the thing you appreciate.

HAVE YOU EVER SEEN BELONGING CREATED WELL IN BOOKS, TV OR MOVIES?
Can you learn anything about your own style of creating belonging by looking at the way your favorite character in TV, movies or books creates belonging for others? What feels life-giving or resonates in you about how this character creates belonging?

Notes

4. Remember: This is not a Round Table exercise, so be sure to meet and share your story with someone who is not a member of your Round Table.

5. You will have 5 minutes. When you are finished, sit back down at your Round Table.

Belonging Exercise: Belonging Rewards
This is a 5 Minute exercise, and your facilitator will lead.

1. Please stay at your Round Table for this exercise.

2. Help your facilitator answer the question: "Who did a great job creating belonging during this exercise?" You – and your facilitator – are free to nominate anyone who did a good job with belonging during the improv. exercises.

3. Your facilitator will award Belonging gifts, and everyone nominated will be recognized and appreciated for their efforts.

4. When this exercise is complete, please restart the video for the second teaching and exercise track: "Knowing When to Stop."

Please restart the Belonging DVD.

Belonging Teaching Track 2: Knowing When to Stop.
• Knowing when to stop can help others keep their RCs running.

Overwhelming others emotionally, verbally or physically with feelings and opinions is controlling – and is something God never does.

We have Jesus' example:
• When He was reviled and insulted, He did not revile or offer insult in return; [when] He was abused and suffered, He made no threats [of vengeance]; but he trusted [Himself and everything] to Him Who judges fairly (1Pe 2:23). Amplified Bible(R) Copyright ©1954, 1958, 1962, 1964, 1965, 1987 by The Lockman Foundation, La Habra, CA 90631. All rights reserved.

God gives us the freedom to chart our own path and make our own choices – even if they are wrong.
• God respects our choices and never overwhelms us by imposing His will on us.

Overwhelming others with our emotions and opinions does not give others this freedom.
• Not knowing when to stop is a root cause of the abusive and controlling use of power by those in positions of authority.

Leadership that overwhelms others emotionally or verbally is abuse – and is not Biblical.
• But sadly, this is often seen in families, churches, ministries, businesses and nations.

GOD NEVER ABUSES HIS POWER - HE KNOWS WHEN TO STOP.
Overwhelming others emotionally, verbally or physically with feelings and opinions is controlling – and is something God never does. He gives us the freedom to chart our own course and make our own choices - even if they are wrong. He respects our choices and does not impose His will upon us.

We need to give others the emotional, relational and physical space to make their own choices. (And we need the same thing!)

Knowing when to stop feels good to us and to others. It creates the space for others to freely belong with us.

When people know when to stop:
- There is no domestic violence, verbal, sexual or emotional abuse.
- Conversations don't produce casualties.
- Criminal behavior doesn't happen.
- People resolve conflicts creatively and resourcefully, and make better decisions under stress, because their RCs are active.
- Freedom flourishes.

Wouldn't the world be a much better and safer place if people just knew when to stop?

When people don't know when to stop:
- Domestic violence, verbal, sexual or emotional abuse flourish.
- Conversations produce casualties.
- Cycles of control, victimization and criminal behavior worsen.
- Conflicts escalate because people make poor decisions and can't think creatively or resourcefully when their RCs are not active.
- Fear, threats and intimidation rule.

Do you really want to be this guy? (Or relate to him when he doesn't stop?)

Do you really want to be this woman? (Or try to relate to her when she doesn't stop?)

Questions:
- What does it feel like when you go too far with others?
- What does it feel like when people go too far with you?

Wouldn't it be great if we could learn to recognize the signs of overwhelm before it happens?
- What are the signs of overwhelm?

Signs of overwhelm in others:
- ❑ Freezing.
- ❑ Small changes in facial expression or body position.
- ❑ Eyes widen, squint or close.
- ❑ No eye contact.
- ❑ A blank expression.
- ❑ Leaning back or backing up.

KNOWING WHEN TO STOP FEELS GOOD TO US AND TO OTHERS.

When we know when to stop, we create the space for others to freely belong with us. Overwhelming others with our feelings and opinions does not give them this freedom, and creates distance instead of belonging. Not knowing when to stop is a root cause of abusive and controlling use of power in relationships and in leadership.

Notes

- ❑ Tears.
- ❑ Muscle tension in brow, nose or body.
- ❑ What else can you think of?
- ❑ _____
- ❑ _____
- ❑ _____
- ❑ _____

Signs of overwhelm in me:

- ❑ Over-talking or talking before thinking.
- ❑ Knots or tightening of stomach, shoulders, face or hands.
- ❑ Backing up or leaning away.
- ❑ Break in eye contact.
- ❑ Feeling numb, going blank, freezing.
- ❑ Leaning forward or crowding.
- ❑ Feeling like "I just want this to stop."
- ❑ Urge to yell, hit, grab, or push.
- ❑ What else can you think of?
- ❑ _____
- ❑ _____
- ❑ _____
- ❑ _____

Are you ready for an exercise to help you learn to know when to stop and avoid overwhelm?

Belonging exercise: Knowing when to stop and avoid overwhelm.
This is a 15 minute exercise, and your facilitator will lead and keep track of time for you.

Introduction: A Water Drinking Race

1. This is a water drinking race to help us learn to watch for the signs of overwhelm and to learn to know when to stop.

2. During this exercise, you will have to form teams, leave your Round Table, get a plastic cup, fill it with water, and line up for the contest. Your facilitator will also help you find the best place to do the exercise and let you know when it's time to start the contest. Because there is so much movement to prepare and experience the water drinking race, please be sure to listen for your facilitator's instructions throughout the exercise.

CAN YOU SPOT THE SIGNS OF OVERWHELM IN YOU AND IN OTHERS?

Learning to recognize the early signs that we - or others - are starting to feel overwhelmed, helps us know that we need to stop. Everything about our interactions with others improves when we recognize the need to stop and restore our RCs - before we totally overwhelm others with too much intensity.

Instructions for the Water Drinking Race:

1. Form groups of 2 from your Round Table. If your Round Table has an odd number of members, you can form a group with someone from another Round Table.

2. Your facilitator and Belonging Coordinator will make sure that everyone receives a plastic cup.

3. Everyone should fill their cup with about 8 oz of water.

4. Go outside (or wherever directed) in your groups of 2 with your glasses of water. Your facilitator will help everyone line up for the exercise.

5. When your facilitator tells you to start, the first person in each group of 2 must drink a glass of water while her or his partner holds the glass. When the first person is finished, the roles switch, and second person drinks a glass of water while his or her partner holds the glass.

6. Be the first team to finish without spilling any water on your partner or the ground!

7. Our goal is to go quickly – and watch for the signs that indicate you are giving your partners enough water without overwhelming them by giving them too much water too quickly.
   a. Only non-verbal communication is allowed during the exercise.
   b. Watch for the non-verbal facial expressions and body language to tell you how fast you can help your partner drink.

9. If you (or the floor) are wet when you are finished, somebody hasn't followed the directions! Goggles and swimsuits are not needed – unless you are overwhelming each other with too much water too quickly!

Belonging Homework: Week 9:

Everyone: Go Overwhelm Watching using your "Knowing When to Stop" worksheet.
- Your worksheet is located on page 142.

Worksheet Part 1:
- Look for the times this week that you think someone needed to pause so that another person could get his or her RCs back on.
- These are the times that someone needed to stop – but kept going anyway.

Worksheet Part 2:
- Watch for the times this week when things were too much, too fast, or too intense and began to overwhelm you or others.
- What signs of overwhelm do you notice?

Note: Be sure to pause and restore your own RCs as needed, especially when you've been overwhelm watching.

Knowing When to Stop Worksheet

Copyright E. James Wilder Ph.D. and Ed Khouri, 2009.

Part One: Look for the times this week that you think someone needed to pause so that another person could get her or his relational circuits back on. These are the times that someone needed to stop...but kept going anyway.

Briefly describe the situation:

How did I know that relational circuits were off? What were the signs?

What happened when there was no chance to stop and turn relational circuits back on?

Part 2: Watch for the times this week when things that were too much, too fast, or too intense began to overwhelm you or others. What signs of overwhelm did you notice?

Briefly describe the overwhelm situation:

There may be physical, emotional and verbal signs that someone is overwhelmed. What signs of overwhelm did you notice? Make a list of all you remember.

Chapter 9: Questions for Further Discussion

1. Please share your answers to these questions that were discussed in small group this week. You can use the Cravings Signs of Attachment Pain Checklist, the Cravings Log, or the Shalom for my Cravings Worksheet to help you answer.
   a. How did you do with shalom, appreciation, RCs, attachment pain and cravings this week?
   b. Did you notice cravings or attachment pain this week?
   c. Did you return to shalom and appreciation with RCs active using our Belonging quieting steps?
   d. How did you quiet?
   e. Were you able to recognize the validation and comfort you received?
   f. What did your emotions and body feel like before and after you quieted and returned to shalom and appreciation with RCs active?

2. What did you learn about your own style of creating belonging this week? What are the gifts, abilities and the characteristics of your heart that can help you create belonging? Make a list of the practical ways that you can start creating and expressing belonging around you right now! Where is the best place for you to start?

3. What happens in relationships when people don't know when to stop? Can you think of examples of times when you or others didn't know when to stop and ended up feeling overwhelmed? Can you think of examples of times when you or others knew when to stop and did feel overwhelmed? Please list at least 3 examples of each, and be sure to describe what each experience felt like, and what happened to the RCs of the people involved.

4. Why does knowing when to stop feel so good to you and to others? What happens when people know when to stop?

5. Are there relationships or situations in which you wish you were better able to stop? What are the relationships? How do you think these relationships would improve if you better knew when to stop?

6. Make a list of the 3 relationships that are closest to you, and think about the signs of overwhelm in others that we discussed in class this week. Next to each name, list the signs you can think of that might indicate that they are beginning to feel overwhelmed.

7. Make a list of the signs that you are starting to feel overwhelmed. Be as specific and detailed as you can be. What happens to your RCs as these signs increase?

8. What were the signs of overwhelm that you noticed in your partner during the water drinking race? How did you know when he or she wanted you to give more - or less - water? How did you communicate that the water was coming too slow - or too fast?

Notes

Belonging Chapter 10:

DO I AMPLIFY OR QUIET NEGATIVE EMOTIONS?
BLOWING UP OR BUILDING UP TRUST AND BELONGING.

Group Opens:
• Ask a volunteer to open the group with prayer.

Belonging exercise: Knowing when to stop review
This is a 15 minute exercise, and your facilitator will keep track of time for you.

1. Please remain at your Round Tables for this exercise.

2. Use your "Knowing when to stop" worksheet, page 142, to share and review your observations of the times that you or others "needed to stop" in the past week.

3. To share and review your observations, please answer the following questions:
   a. How did it affect your sense of belonging when others stopped listening – or turned off their relational circuits?
   b. How could you tell that relational circuits in you or others were off?

5. You may find it helpful to use examples from last week's water drinking contest to explain what happened when relational circuits were overwhelmed.

Please start the Belonging DVD for this week's lesson.

Belonging Teaching: Do I amplify or quiet negative emotions? Blowing up or building up trust and belonging.

What does "Belonging" look like?
• Belonging is the joy we create around us!

Belonging is Training!

Weekly Bible Story: Grasshoppers in my eyes: Amplifying negative feelings – or quieting and building shalom (Numbers 13-14)

To know when to stop, my relational circuits must be working!

My RCs help me to:
• Grow capacity by living in shalom & appreciation.
• Know when to stop when I'm upset so that I don't amplify my distress.
• Keep from overwhelming you.
• Give us room to quiet, build shalom and create belonging together.
• Help you keep your relational circuits on.
• Build trust with you.

> ## TO KNOW WHEN TO STOP, MY RELATIONAL CIRCUITS MUST BE WORKING.
> *Otherwise, I will overwhelm you, and not even realize I've done it - until it's too late!*

Notes

When my relational circuits are off, I amplify my distress and negative emotions, so I:
- Don't know when to stop.
- Don't even notice I need to stop.
- Don't realize the effect I am having on others.
- Blame others for my distress and problems.
- Overwhelm people and cause their RCs to shut down.
- Lose the trust of others.

What are the warning signs? How can I tell when I'm just about to "lose it" or if I'm already amplifying negative emotions?

Warning Signs:
- ❑ Rapid, shallow breaths.
- ❑ Pounding head and heart.
- ❑ Muscles in my shoulders tighten, my fists and muscles clench and my stomach in a knot.
- ❑ My thoughts and negative feelings race.
- ❑ I feel an enormous amount of energy running through my body right now...and I can't make it stop.
- ❑ I am trying to figure out what to say before you finish talking.
- ❑ I interrupt you before you finish talking.
- ❑ It feels like I have to make this stop right now!
- ❑ I am not aware of – or don't care – how my reactions will affect you.
- ❑ I feel like I want to punish you for making me feel this way.
- ❑ I feel the rising urge to hit, grab, shove or push you to make it stop and get back in control.
- ❑ I don't feel God's presence with us.
- ❑ I cannot tell the difference between you and the problem.
- ❑ It is hard to think about you as someone I care about right now.
- ❑ I don't want to think about stopping so we can deal with this later. This has to be resolved now!
- ❑ I need to prove my point and win.
- ❑ I really can't tell how you are reacting to me right now.
- ❑ If my reactions are hurting you, it's because you deserve it for what you've done and for making me feel this way!
- ❑ I have tunnel vision about this situation and I can't think creatively about how to use my resources to solve this problem.
- ❑ I over talk.
- ❑ My voice is loud, louder, loudest.

WHAT ARE THE WARNING SIGNS THAT YOU ARE ABOUT TO "LOSE IT?"
By learning to identify the signs that we are amplifying - and not quieting - negative emotions, we help other people keep their RCs online. If I miss the warning signs and amplify my negative emotions, I am likely to cause your RCs to shut down.

Notes

What other warning signs can you think of? What does it look like when you or other people amplify negative emotions?

❏ _____

❏ _____

❏ _____

❏ _____

❏ _____

If I miss the warning signs, I am likely to keep amplifying distress until your RCs go offline.
- Now, both of us are overwhelmed.
- We've lost shalom and appreciation, and neither of us has working RCs!

Really bad things happen when 2 non-relational brains collide!
- When we don't have a working relational circuit between us, it's not usually a pretty sight.
- Is this what your heart really wants?

What our heart really wants is appreciation, shalom, quiet together, trust and belonging.

Knowing when to stop and quieting together are the basis for trust!

Knowing when to stop builds trust.
- If you know when to stop and don't overwhelm me, I can trust you.
- If you don't know when to stop and you overwhelm me, I can't trust you!

I build trust in my relationships when I:
- Keep my RCs on.
- Recognize the early signs of overwhelm in you and stop before I provoke fear, anxiety and anger in you.
- Allow us the chance to rest and quiet our distress together before we go any further.

Where do you want to go? Do you want to switch off your RCs or move towards shalom?

It's simple.
- If you want people to trust you, then you must deal with the tendency to overwhelm others – and learn to stop!

What builds trust and belonging?
- Quieting to share shalom and appreciation together or blowing out relational circuits?

We can learn to stop and quiet together.
- With appreciation, shalom and our RCs active, trust and relationships grow.
- Belonging will flourish!

IT'S SIMPLE: KNOWING WHEN TO STOP BUILDS TRUST.
If you know when to stop and don't overwhelm me, I can trust you.
If you don't know when to stop and you overwhelm me, I can't trust you.
I build trust in relationships when I know when to stop - before I overwhelm you!

Notes

Belonging Exercise: Growing trust and knowing when to stop.
This is a 12 minute class discussion exercise, and your facilitator will lead.

1. Please remain at your Round Tables as your facilitator leads you in a short class discussion.
2. You will have 3 minutes to answer each of the following, so please follow your facilitator's instructions and the directions in your workbook to keep your answers brief. By following the directions and keeping your answers brief, you create Belonging by giving more class members time to share.
   a. Are there places where you think trust is needed for better belonging around you at home, work or with friends? Use 1 sentence to answer.
   b. Describe the times you often feel like "that's enough" or just want someone to stop. Use 1 sentence to answer.
   c. How do I feel when I need to take a break? Use 1 or 2 words to answer.
   d. What is my youngest memory of "tuning out?" (Tuning out is often a sign of overwhelm.) Use 1 or 2 words to answer.
3. Your facilitator will let you know when it's time for the next exercise.

Belonging Exercise: Knowing when to stop.
This is a 10 minute exercise, and your facilitator will keep track of time for you.

1. Please remain at your Round Tables for this exercise.
2. In this exercise, you will have 10 minutes to answer the questions listed below in your Round Tables.
   a. What do people mean when they say "you are yelling?"
   b. What are the signs of "yelling?"
   c. What are the short term effects of "yelling?"
   d. What are the long term effects of "yelling?"

Belonging Exercise: Quieting through appreciation.
This is a 10 minute Round Table exercise with 2 parts. Each part is 5 minutes long, and your facilitator will keep track of time for you.

1. Please stay at your Round Table and follow your facilitator's instructions for both parts of this exercise.
2. Part 1: At your Round Tables, take 5 minutes to reflect on your list of appreciation memories, 5 bar moments and gifts from God and find a strong sense of appreciation.
   a. Please reflect on these moments and memories silently.
   b. Remember: 5 bar moments are times when we felt a strong connection with God or had a strong sense of His presence.
3. Part 2: Take 5 minutes for everyone at your Round Table to describe the effects of the appreciation they just felt by using one word to complete these phrases:
   a. Before feeling the appreciation I felt _____.
   b. After appreciation, I felt _____.

WHAT DO PEOPLE MEAN WHEN THEY SAY "YOU ARE YELLING?"
What are the signs that you are yelling?
What are the short and long term effects of "yelling?"
Sometimes, is it hard for you to even notice that you are "yelling?"

Belonging Exercise: Star Cards: Class Belonging Project

This exercise introduces the Belonging Star Card Class Project, and is a total of 25 minutes long. It has 4 parts, and your facilitator will keep track of time for you in each section.

Exercise Overview:

1. This is a 4 part exercise that introduces the Belonging Class Star Card Project. Please follow the directions in your workbook and your facilitator's instructions throughout the exercise.

2. In this exercise, you will be working at your Round Table and in groups of 3 as follows:
   a. Part 1: Introduction: Round Table. (5 minutes)
   b. Part 2: Handing out Star Cards: Round Table. (5 minutes)
   c. Part 3: Small Group Discussion: Small groups of 3 from your Round Table. (10 minutes)
   d. Part 4: Round Table Discussion: Round Table. (5 minutes)

3. Your facilitator will keep track of time for you throughout the exercise.

Part 1: Star Card Introduction (5 Minutes)

1. To start, stay at your Round Table and your Facilitator and Belonging Coordinator will give each of you Star Cards.

2. Listen and follow along in your workbook as your facilitator introduces and explains the project.

3. The purpose of the Star Card Project is to:
   a. Help you learn to spot people outside of our Belonging class who do a good job of creating belonging and reward them.
   b. Express appreciation to them in your own style.

4. Our Star Card Project goals are to:
   a. Improve our ability to spot those who are doing a good job at expressing belonging to others.
   b. Further identify our own style of expressing belonging through watching the example of others who create belonging well.
   c. Practice our belonging skills outside of class.
   d. Create belonging for others through appreciation.
   e. Increase our own skills at expressing appreciation using our own personal style.

5. Star Card Instructions: At church this Sunday, when you see people create belonging:
   a. Introduce yourself, and tell them that you are part of the Belonging class.
   b. Explain that one of our class goals is to learn how to create a joyful place for others to belong around us – and learn to express it.
   c. Hand them a Star Card and tell them why you appreciate the belonging you just saw them express and why it was important for you.
   d. Thank them...and move on!

Part 2: Handing out Star Cards (5 Minutes).

1. Please stay at your Round Table for this part of the exercise as your facilitator reviews what you can say when you hand out Star Cards.

2. If you aren't sure what to say when you hand out a Star Card, you can use this script:
   a. Hi. My name is _____ and I am part of the Belonging class.

> ### THE STAR CARD PROJECT:
> *Helps us practice our belonging skills outside of class and express appreciation.
> It also allows us to further identify our own style of creating belonging
> by finding and watching the example of people who create belonging well.*

Notes

    b. One of our goals in class is to learn how to create a joyful place for others to belong with us, and to be able to express that to them.

    c. Hand them a Star Card.

    d. I just saw you create belonging when you _____, and I appreciate it because _____. This was important for me because_____.

    e. Thank you!

Part 3: Small Group Discussion (10 Minutes).

1. Please form groups of 3 from your Round Table.

2. When you have formed your groups, share your answers to these questions:

    a. Is there anything about this project that makes you feel anxious?

    b. If you are not in a church, where else could you do this project?

    c. Do you need help deciding where to do this?

3. Share your responses, encourage and help each other!

Part 4: Round Table Sharing (5 Minutes).

1. Please return to your Round Tables for this part of the exercise.

2. Share the location where you will hand out your Star Cards with your Coordinator and Round Table members.

3. Your Belonging Coordinator will use the "Star Card Location List" to note the location each person chooses, page 151.

4. Your Belonging Coordinator will send you an email reminding you about the Star Card Project this week.

5. Email your good experiences giving out the cards to each other and to your Coordinator this week!

Belonging Homework: Week 10

Coordinators:

• Send an email reminder to Round Table members about the Star Card Project.

Everyone:

Star Card Project
• Hand out Star Cards at church or your other target location this week.
• Email each other with good experiences you've had when handing out your cards!

Go Shalom Watching
• Keep using your Shalom Watching Worksheet, pages 152-153.
• Watch for signs of overwhelm when you or others need to stop and quiet.
• Then, use the steps you've learned to quiet and restore RCs, shalom and appreciation.

Coordinators: Round Table Star Card Location List
©Copyright E. James Wilder Ph.D. and Ed Khouri, 2009.

Instructions: This week, your Round Table members will begin the class Star Card project, and will hand out Star Cards at church or another location of their choosing. Use this form to list the location that each member of your Round Table has chosen to hand out Star Cards this week.

This week, send an email to all the members of your Round Table reminding them of the Star Card project and the location they have chosen.

Name	Star Card Project Location

Go Shalom, Appreciation and RC Watching

A five-day log of observations about shalom, appreciation and my relational circuits
© Copyright E. James Wilder Ph.D. and Ed Khouri, 2009.

Instructions:

Each day, use this form to keep track of shalom, appreciation and your RCs. Briefly describe when you noticed that shalom, appreciation and your RCs were fading, and how the problem began. Next, place a check next to every statement that describes what happened when you lost shalom, appreciation and your RCs, then place a check next to each step you used to restore them. Finally, write one word that best describes what it felt like emotionally and in your body when you lost shalom, appreciation and your RCs – and when they were restored.

Day 1: When did I notice that my shalom, appreciation and RCs faded? What started these fading?

What happened when I lost shalom, appreciation and my RCs?	
____ Attachment pain was involved.	____ My cravings increased.
____ I lost Godsight.	____ I stopped creating Belonging.
Which of the following steps did I use to restore shalom, appreciation and my RCs?	
____ RC Checklist ____ Shalom for my Body ____ Shalom for my Soul & Heart	
The emotion validated was _____	The comfort was _____
When my shalom, appreciation and RCs faded:	**When shalom, appreciation & RCs were restored:**
The emotion I felt was _____	The emotion I felt was _____
My body felt _____	My body felt _____

Day 2: When did I notice that my shalom, appreciation and RCs faded? What started these fading?

What happened when I lost shalom, appreciation and my RCs?	
____ Attachment pain was involved.	____ My cravings increased.
____ I lost Godsight.	____ I stopped creating Belonging.
Which of the following steps did I use to restore shalom, appreciation and my RCs?	
____ RC Checklist ____ Shalom for my Body ____ Shalom for my Soul & Heart	
The emotion validated was _____	The comfort was _____
When my shalom, appreciation and RCs faded:	**When shalom, appreciation & RCs were restored:**
The emotion I felt was _____	The emotion I felt was _____
My body felt _____	My body felt _____

Day 3: When did I notice that my shalom, appreciation and RCs faded? What started these fading?

What happened when I lost shalom, appreciation and my RCs?		
___ Attachment pain was involved.	___ My cravings increased.	
___ I lost Godsight.	___ I stopped creating Belonging.	
Which of the following steps did I use to restore shalom, appreciation and my RCs?		
___ RC Checklist	___ Shalom for my Body	___ Shalom for my Soul & Heart
The emotion validated was _____	The comfort was _____	
When my shalom, appreciation and RCs faded:	**When shalom, appreciation & RCs were restored:**	
The emotion I felt was _____	The emotion I felt was _____	
My body felt _____	My body felt _____	

Day 4: When did I notice that my shalom, appreciation and RCs faded? What started these fading?

What happened when I lost shalom, appreciation and my RCs?		
___ Attachment pain was involved.	___ My cravings increased.	
___ I lost Godsight.	___ I stopped creating Belonging.	
Which of the following steps did I use to restore shalom, appreciation and my RCs?		
___ RC Checklist	___ Shalom for my Body	___ Shalom for my Soul & Heart
The emotion validated was _____	The comfort was _____	
When my shalom, appreciation and RCs faded:	**When shalom, appreciation & RCs were restored:**	
The emotion I felt was _____	The emotion I felt was _____	
My body felt _____	My body felt _____	

Day 5: When did I notice that my shalom, appreciation and RCs faded? What started these fading?

What happened when I lost shalom, appreciation and my RCs?		
___ Attachment pain was involved.	___ My cravings increased.	
___ I lost Godsight.	___ I stopped creating Belonging.	
Which of the following steps did I use to restore shalom, appreciation and my RCs?		
___ RC Checklist	___ Shalom for my Body	___ Shalom for my Soul & Heart
The emotion validated was _____	The comfort was _____	
When my shalom, appreciation and RCs faded:	**When shalom, appreciation & RCs were restored:**	
The emotion I felt was _____	The emotion I felt was _____	
My body felt _____	My body felt _____	

Notes

Chapter 10: Questions for Further Discussion

1. Share your experiences with the Knowing When To Stop Worksheet this week and make a list of the signs that you or others were starting to feel overwhelmed. If you started to feel overwhelmed, how did you restore your RCs? What happened to belonging when you or others were feeling overwhelmed?

2. Why is knowing when to stop essential for building trust?

3. When you were growing up, did people in your family amplify negative emotions? Did amplifying negative emotions feel and seem normal to you? Were you able to trust those who amplified negative emotions? Do you see the same patterns of amplifying and trust in your relationships today?

4. Why do you amplify negative emotions when your RCs are off? Can you think of a time recently when you amplified negative emotions? Describe what happened, and how this affected you and the people around you. Were you able to restore your RCs later?

5. Make a detailed list of all the signs that you are amplifying negative emotions. Who are the people most affected when you amplify negative emotions? What do you think you can do to improve or restore these relationships? Please note: sometimes more healing is needed before we can improve damaged relationships, and you will begin to address these issues in the Healing and Loving modules.

6. How can you better build trust in relationships that are important to you? Are there specific steps that you are able to take now that would help you? List the relationships and the steps.

7. Describe the times you often feel like "that's enough" or you just want someone to stop. What does it feel like when you need to "stop and take a break?"

8. "Tuning out" is often a sign that we are overwhelmed and are trying to disengage from others. When and how do you "tune out?" Are there specific relationships in which you tend to "tune out" more than others? When did you first learn to "tune out" to cope with overwhelm? Does "tuning out" really work for you when you are overwhelmed?

9. Do people sometimes tell you that you are "yelling?" Remember a time in which this happened and think about what you were doing. Were you amplifying distressing emotions and how did you communicate your feelings? How did this affect the people around you? As you reflect on this memory, can you identify any of the warning signs that you were about to amplify your distress? Describe anything you would want to do differently now if a similar situation occurs.

Notes

Notes

Belonging Chapter 11:

WHEN QUIET IS NOT QUIETING.

DO I REALLY QUIET NEGATIVE EMOTIONS, OR DO I JUST HIDE FROM DISTRESSING FEELINGS AND DISMISS PEOPLE WHEN THEY ARE UPSET?

Group Opens:
• Ask a volunteer to open the group with prayer.

Belonging exercise: Star Card Report
This is a 10 minute exercise, and your facilitator will keep track of time for you.

1. Please form groups of 3 from your Round Tables.

2. Share your experiences with the Star Card Project and encourage each other for your efforts.

3. Please use these questions to guide you as you share:
   a. What did you learn about your own style of creating belonging?
   b. How did you feel when you expressed appreciation for those who created belonging?
   c. Would you do anything differently next time?

4. You will have 10 minutes, and your facilitator will let you know when it's time for the next exercise.

Belonging Exercise: Let's try Star Cards again!
This is a 5 minute exercise, and your facilitator will keep track of time for you.

1. Please return to your Round Table, and your facilitator and Belonging Coordinator will give you more Star Cards.

2. Incorporate anything you learned from last week's experiences, and repeat the Star Card Exercise again this week.

3. Email each other with the good experiences you have as you hand out the cards.

Belonging exercise: Class Project: Create Belonging at Church for the Pastor and for the Person who Answers the Phone at Church.
This is a 5 minute exercise, and your facilitator will keep track of time for you.

1. Please remain at your Round Table for project instructions.

2. This week, our Belonging class has a new project: to create belonging at church for the pastor and for the person who answers the phone at church.

3. Your facilitator will help each Round Table choose a gift from the lists we've used to create and express belonging here in class. Gifts could include:
   a. A flower.
   b. A snack you like to share.
   c. A Blessing Card you made.
   d. Collect prayer requests and then pray for them.

QUIETING IS VERY DIFFERENT FROM DISMISSING, IGNORING OR HIDING FROM DIFFICULT PEOPLE OR DISTRESSING EMOTIONS!

Notes

4. Each Round Table should select their appreciation gift and then decide how to give their gifts to the Pastor and the person who answers the phone at church this week.

5. Your Coordinator will:
   a. Use the "Creating Belonging for the Pastor and Person who Answers the Phone at Church" worksheet to make a list of your Table's plans, page 164.
   b. Email a project reminder to Round Table members this week.

6. You will have 5 minutes, and your facilitator will keep track of time for you.

Please start the Belonging DVD for this week's lesson.

Belonging Teaching: Do I really quiet negative emotions, or do I just hide from distressing feelings and dismiss people when they are upset?

What does "Belonging" look like?
• Belonging is the joy we create around us!

Belonging is Training!

Week 11 Bible Story: Am I quieting or dismissing with God and others? 1 Samuel 25
• Nabal the fool dismisses,
• David the hothead amplifies,
• Abigail the wise quiets.

To know when to stop and quiet, my RCs must be working!
• Learning to monitor and restore my RCs as I interact with others is a vital relational skill.
• This skill is essential if I want to know when to stop and when to quiet with you.

Quieting:
• Keeps me in shalom and gives my brain a chance to rest, recover and fully engage my RCs if I am starting to feel overwhelmed.
• Allows me to access the relational, creative and problem solving areas of my brain needed to handle difficult emotions, conflict and problems.

Quieting restores. It doesn't ignore.
• Quieting restores me to shalom and helps me restore the relational circuits I need to stay relational and solve problems.
• Quieting does not mean that I can return to shalom and then ignore and dismiss the emotions, problems, people and conflicts in a relationship.

Is there a difference between quieting and shutting down?
• From the outside, quieting & shutting down may look the same.
• But they are complete opposites, and lead to very different outcomes!

QUIETING RESTORES - IT DOESN'T IGNORE.
If I am feeling overwhelmed, quieting restores me to shalom and appreciation with my RCs active. Dismissing means that I am ignoring and avoiding difficult feelings or people with problems. Shalom, appreciation and my RCs all fade.

How can I know if I am quieting – or dismissing – the importance of feelings, thoughts, people or conflicts in relationships?

Quieting:

- ❑ I am aware of God's presence – that He is with me and cares about my feelings and problem.

- ❑ The muscles in my face, around my eyes and in my body relax.

- ❑ My breathing is deep.

- ❑ My stomach is not in a knot, and tension eases in my shoulders.

- ❑ I notice the emotions that I am feeling, and I am aware of yours.

- ❑ I care about your feelings & opinions.

- ❑ My distressing emotions are quieting, and Godsight helps me think more clearly about them – and us.

- ❑ I remember why I appreciate you.

- ❑ Relational or emotional isolation doesn't feel like a good idea.

- ❑ Resolving the problem and staying relational feels important to me and is something I want to do.

- ❑ I think creatively and resourcefully about you and the problem.

- ❑ What other signs of quieting can you think of?

- ❑ _____

- ❑ _____

- ❑ _____

- ❑ _____

Dismissing:

- ❑ I am not particularly aware of God's presence with me, and I lack Godsight.

- ❑ My face may not show much emotion, but the muscles in my face are tight.

- ❑ My shoulders, body and stomach are in a knot – and my breathing is shallow.

- ❑ I may recognize that you are upset, but I don't understand what you are feeling or why you are so upset.

- ❑ I am not very aware of what I feel or why the problem is important to us.

- ❑ I just want this to be over, and feel the urge to run away, hide, disappear and isolate.

- ❑ When I think about resolving the problem or engaging with you, I feel dread and hopelessness that logic won't fix.

- ❑ My cravings for BEEPS and relief get stronger.

- ❑ When I feel overwhelmed, I create emotional and relational distance from you & others.

> ### AMPLIFIER - DISMISSIVE CONFLICTS ARE PAINFUL.
> *When dismissive partners create distance in relationships to avoid others who are experiencing painful emotions, their relational partners are often likely to respond by amplifying negative emotions in an effort to "make" the dismissive "pay attention."*

Notes

❑ My thinking is not creative or resourceful.

❑ I can't think of why I value or appreciate you – you just seem like a problem.

❑ What other signs of dismissing can you think of?

❑ _____

❑ _____

❑ _____

❑ _____

Recognizing the need for quiet is vital for belonging.
- Learning to stop and quiet is important because it can keep us from overwhelming others – and helps us quiet our own distressing emotions.
- When we recognize that others also need to quiet, we can give them the space they need to stay relational with us.

But what happens if we, or a relationship partner, are dismissive?
- The dismissive partner is likely to feel overwhelmed, and creates emotional and relational distance in the relationship.
- Problems are unresolved and grow, frustrating the non-dismissive partner.
- The non-dismissive partner then often increasingly amplifies negative emotions in an effort to make his or her partner "pay attention."
- This creates an interesting scenario.

Amplifier – Dismissive conflicts are painful!

Increased amplitude causes increased shut down.
- Amplitude may be able to provoke temporary change, but will not produce positive emotional and relational growth.
- It will result in increasing shut down, avoidance, distance, and frustration – and will eventually kill the relationship.

Shalom and quiet do not mean there will be no problems.
- Peaceful relationships where nothing ever happens are not the same thing as shalom.
- If nothing ever happens, it's probably a good indicator that something in the relationship is shut down or dead.

Whether I amplify or dismiss, change always begins with appreciation, shalom, quieting and <u>my</u> RCs.
- If I am hiding from negative emotions and dismiss people who are distressed, it is usually because I've lost shalom and appreciation and my RCs are off.
- If I am increasing the amplitude of my negative emotions to get someone to respond to me, it is usually because I've lost shalom and appreciation and my RCs are off.

Change always begins when I focus on my RCs, and not yours!

> **INCREASED AMPLITUDE CAUSES INCREASED SHUT DOWN.**
> *Amplifying negative emotions may produce temporary change.*
> *It does not produce long term positive emotional and relational growth.*
> *Amplifying only leads to greater relational distance, mistrust and frustration.*

I cannot make your relational circuits behave the way I want them to.
- I am much better off working on my ability to quiet and restore my RCs – and letting God work with you and your RCs.
- If I stop overwhelming you and allow you to quiet, there is a better chance that you will actually want to relate to me anyway – and allow God to help!

Quieting and knowing when to stop all start with my own RCs.

Get ready for two new "knowing when to stop" exercises.
- But first, an important announcement about next week's Belonging class and a very special homework assignment:

Belonging Party!
- Next week is our closing Belonging party.
- Bring some of your favorite snacks, munchies and drinks to share as we celebrate, chow down, tell stories and create belonging together!
- You'll be telling appreciation stories while you munch on tasty treats, so be sure to complete your Appreciation Story Worksheet and bring it with you next week.

Belonging exercise: Knowing when to stop, Exercise 1: The Penny Toss
This exercise is 35 minutes, and has several parts. Your facilitator will lead and keep track of time for you.

Introduction: The Penny Toss Exercise

1. The Penny Toss Exercise is a contest between Round Tables and has several sections.

2. You will be forming teams and moving around the classroom for part of this exercise, so please be sure to follow your facilitator's instructions as she or he leads you.

3. Each Round Table must choose 6 members for their team, and if possible, each team should consist of 3 men and 3 women.

4. After you've chosen your teams, your facilitator will give you further instructions.

Penny Toss set-up

1. Help your facilitator get ready for the contest by:
   a. Arranging tables and the room for the contest (if needed).
   b. Listening to directions to help each Round Table team line up and get ready to start the Penny Toss.

2. Your facilitator and Coordinator will make sure that each team receives 15 pennies.

3. Each team should designate a thrower and a catcher to start the penny toss.

4. The thrower and catcher should stand facing each other 10 feet apart and the catcher should have a table behind her or him.

5. The other members of your team should be lined up behind the thrower.

> ### Good News for Codependents:
> *Change always begins when I focus on my RCs - and not yours.*
> *I can't make your RCs behave the way I want them to.*
> *I can learn to live in shalom and appreciation with my RCs increasingly active.*

Notes

Penny Toss directions

1. The thrower tosses the first penny to the catcher who must catch the penny and stack it on the table behind her or him. This means you have to turn away while stacking the penny!

2. When all the pennies are stacked, the catcher moves to the end of the thrower line and the thrower moves to the catcher side.

3. The next person in line becomes the new thrower and repeats the cycle.

4. Each person in line takes a turn as both a thrower and catcher.

5. Since the first person to catch pennies is the last person in the line, the game is over when this person finishes his or her turn as thrower.

6. Your facilitator will make sure that each team understands this rotation before the contest starts.

7. Important Note: If at any time, your stack of pennies falls over, you must stop and restack them before continuing.

The Penny Toss winners:

1. The first team to have all players finish with all of their pennies stacked wins!

2. After a short period of wildly enthusiastic celebration and congratulations for everyone involved, return to your Round Tables for a quick RC check and Part Two of this exercise.

A quick RC Check: How are your RCs after the penny toss?

1. Please make sure you have returned to your Round Table for this quick RC Check.

2. Complete your short-form RC Checklist:
   - ❑ I just want to make a problem, person or feeling go away.
   - ❑ I don't want to listen to what others feel or say.
   - ❑ My mind is "locked onto" something upsetting.
   - ❑ I don't want to be connected to? (someone I usually like)
   - ❑ I just want to get away, or fight or I freeze.
   - ❑ I more aggressively interrogate, judge and fix others.

Penny Toss Round Table discussion and questions:

1. Please remain at your Round Table for this part of the Penny Toss Exercise.

2. Please share your answers to these questions with your Round Table:
   a. How could you know when to pause and when to throw?
   b. How did it feel if someone threw too soon, too hard, or too fast?
   c. How did it feel when your toss was dropped?
   d. How does pressure and lack of time make us rush our timing?
   e. What can we learn about helping others hear us and helping them keep their relational circuits on?

3. Your facilitator will keep track of time for you, and let you know when it's time to start the next exercise.

NEXT WEEK: OUR BELONGING PARTY

Next week is our final session of belonging, and to celebrate, we're having a party! Prepare some appreciation stories, and bring some of your favorite snacks, munchies and drinks to share as we celebrate our belonging!

Belonging exercise: Knowing when to stop Exercise 2: How can I tell when people have stopped listening?

This is a 15 minute discussion exercise, and your facilitator will keep track of time for you.

1. Please remain at your Round Table, for this exercise.

2. Share your answers to these questions with your Round Table: How can I tell when people have stopped listening? What are the signs?

3. Make a list of the signs that your Round Table discovered.

4. When your Table has finished making a list of the signs that people have stopped listening, volunteers may demonstrate the signs using Level 4 stories. If there is time, show your stories to the whole class.
   a. Level 4 Stories are stories told without words, and use only facial expression, body language and movement to communicate.
   b. Unlike Level 4+ stories that include words, Level 4 stories use the non-verbal control center in the right hemisphere of the brain to communicate.

5. Please note: Overwhelm signs are usually involuntary.
   a. Overwhelm signs are usually involuntary and only show up clearly when we are triggered.
   b. This means that when we aren't feeling overwhelmed, we're often unaware of what we actually look like when we're feeling overwhelmed.
   c. Do your best with this exercise. It's OK to demonstrate and explain what you think you might look like when you are overwhelmed.

6. You have 15 minutes for this exercise, and your facilitator will keep track of time for you.

Belonging Homework: Week 11

Belonging Coordinators:

• Email Round Table members and remind them of the plan to create belonging for the Pastor and person who answers the phone at church.

Everyone:

Create Belonging for the Pastor and person who answers the phone at church:
• Give your gifts this week.

Star Card Class Project:
• Remember to continue the class Star Card Project by handing out your Star Cards to people at church or your target location who do a good job creating belonging this week!
• Encourage each other by emailing stories of positive Star Card Experiences.

Week 12 Worksheets: Please complete and bring these worksheets to class with you next week.
• Appreciation Stories, page 165: Be ready to tell stories about things we've learned and experienced in Belonging. You can include Star Card stories too!
• Belonging Class Evaluation Form, pages 166-167: Your feedback is important!

Belonging Party:
• Next week is our closing Belonging party.
• Bring some of your favorite snacks, munchies and drinks to share as we celebrate, chow down, tell stories and create belonging together!

Coordinators: Creating Belonging for the Pastor and Person who Answers the Phone at Church Worksheet

©Copyright E. James Wilder Ph.D. and Ed Khouri, 2009.

Instructions:

In this week's project, your Round Table will create Belonging for the Pastor and for the person who answers the phone at church by selecting an appreciation gift and giving it to them.

Please remind members to prepare their expression of belonging with as much of their own personal style as will fit with the idea your Round Table chooses. Your table should pick one of the ideas listed below and discussed in class.

Use this form to list the gift your table chooses – and how they want to give their gift. List the names of persons who are bringing the gift – and how your group will give the gift.

Be sure to send an email to your Round Table members reminding them of the project – and express appreciation to them for participating!

My Round Table has chosen to create belonging by giving: (check your table's choice)

- ❑ A flower.
- ❑ A snack you like to share.
- ❑ A blessing card you make.
- ❑ Collecting prayer requests from the pastor and phone person – and praying for them.

Our Round Table will give our gift by:

Members who are bringing the gifts:

Members who will be giving the gifts:

Week 12 Worksheets: Appreciation & Class Evaluation

©Copyright E. James Wilder Ph.D. and Ed Khouri, 2009.

Instructions:
This worksheet has 2 parts: the Week 12 Appreciation Story Worksheet and the Belonging Class Evaluation. The Appreciation Story Worksheet is found below, and the Belonging Class Evaluation Form starts on the next page. You will need both for next week's class.

Appreciation Story Worksheet

Take the materials/food provided in the classroom (and any you bring) and create belonging.

Share:

1. What did I learn about creating belonging during this class?

2. What did I learn about my style of creating belonging?

Prepare to tell some appreciation stories (in a four plus way) to create your style of belonging.

❑ Say what I appreciated.

❑ Make my description of the situation brief.

❑ This story is about me (autobiographical), and I am involved in telling the story.

❑ I show my genuine emotions on my face and in my voice when telling the story.

❑ I keep eye contact with my listeners while storytelling.

❑ I include words for my emotions.

❑ I describe what my body felt like.

❑ I describe appreciation enough for others to know how it feels.

❑ I say what is it like me to do when I am creating belonging once again.

❑ This story begins and ends with my feeling appreciation.

Topics for My Appreciation Stories

1. What did I know about creating belonging before this class and what do I know now?
2. What do I appreciate about my RCs when they are running better?
3. What have I learned about cravings and attachment needs that has helped me grow?
4. What have I learned about helping others keep their RCs on?
5. What do I appreciate about my style for creating belonging?
6. What do I appreciate about the belonging I have created and received in this class?
7. What do I appreciate about my Belonging round table group and classmates?
8. Appreciation stories from my Godsight moments.
9. Good things that came out of our class Star Card project.

Work your way around the room telling stories. Talk to as many people you do not know as possible in the remaining time.

Notes

Belonging Class Evaluation

Please complete this form and turn it back in before the end of the final Belonging Class.

- ❑ I attended Forming before taking this class.
- ❑ I attended Restarting before taking this class.
- ❑ I attended a THRIVE conference before taking this class.
- ❑ I have attended a 12 step program.
- ❑ I was invited to Belonging but had no Thriving Recovery class experience before this.
- ❑ I have experienced healing prayer ministry.
- ❑ I intend to go on to Healing.

1. How many of the 12 classes in Belonging did you attend? _____.
2. If you missed classes what were the reasons?

3. How many appreciation moments did you write down during the 12 weeks? _____.
4. What percentage of the classes you attended did you arrive with your relational circuits struggling (RC function weak or off)? _____%
5. What percentage of your day do you estimate your relational circuits were having trouble before you began this Belonging class? _____%.
6. What is your percentage now at week 12? _____%
7. What was your practice time per week for Belonging exercises? _____

How many times did you practice (or use) each of the following?
_____ ThrivingRecovery.org website downloads
_____ The full Relational Circuits Checklist
_____ Short form Relational Circuits checklist (on business card)
_____ Cravings Signs for Attachment Pain. How many cravings did you check off? _____
_____ Unrecognized Attachment Pain Checklist. How many BEEPS signs did you check?_____

How many times did you do the entire Shalom for my Body Long Form exercise? (as found in the appendix) _____

_____ Fear Bomb
_____ First Aid Yawn
_____ Deep Breathing Relaxation

How many times did you do the Belonging Quieting Steps?
_____ Shalom for my Body
_____ Shalom for my Soul
_____ Shalom for my Heart
_____ Grow my Appreciation

Notes

Relational Circuits Questions

How many weeks did you do the Shalom Watching Worksheet? _____
How many weeks did you fill out the Shalom Watching Worksheet? _____
How many days did you use the Shalom Watching Worksheet on your best practice week? _____
What was helpful and what was difficult about using the Shalom Watching Worksheet?

What were your results from the RC exercises and Shalom Watching Worksheet?

How many times did you do the Shalom for my Cravings exercise? _____ What were the results?

Of all the exercises in Belonging, what exercises were the most helpful to you and why?

What have you learned in Belonging and then told/taught to others outside the class and why?

What aspects of the Belonging class were unhelpful to you and why?

What would you do to improve your results from Belonging if you were to take it again?

Who would you tell about or send to a Belonging class and why?

What would you tell someone about the Belonging class?

Notes

Chapter 11: Questions for Further Discussion

1. Abigail, David and Nabal each had a different response to a situation that upset them. Which person's response is most typically like your own? Why?

2. From your own experience, what are the important differences between quieting and shutting down? Make a list of at least 10.

3. Can you think of an example of a time in which you quieted and a time when you dismissed? What did it feel like when you quieted, and what did it feel like when you dismissed? What were the outcomes of each, and how did they affect your relationships and ability to create belonging?

4. List at least 5 signs that you are quieting.

5. List at least 5 signs that you are dismissing.

6. Have you ever been in a dismissive-amplifier conflict in an important relationship? Which role did you play? Describe what you did and how effective it was in resolving the conflict. How long did it take for the unresolved conflict to return?

7. Can you think of a relationship right now in which you have spent a lot of energy trying to get another person to "behave" or respond to you differently? Describe the relationship, and the strategies you've tried to use in an effort to "make" him or her relate to you differently. What do you think would happen in the relationship if you focused your energy on strengthening your own RCs, shalom and appreciation. List the specific steps you could start with right now.

8. What did you learn about "knowing when to stop" from the Penny Toss Exercise? What did you learn about communicating with your partner when both of you were hurried and pressured? What did you do to help your partner hear you - and what did your partner do to help you hear him or her? How did you help each other keep your RCs on?

9. What does it mean when people have "stopped listening?" What are the signs that you have stopped listening? List 3 relationships that are important to you, and list the signs that they have stopped listening.

Notes

Notes

Belonging Chapter 12:

WE BELONG!

WHAT KINDS OF THINGS DID WE LEARN
AND EXPERIENCE TOGETHER IN BELONGING?

Group Opens:
- Ask a volunteer to open the group with prayer.

Belonging Teaching: What have we experienced together, and where do we go from here?

What kinds of things did we learn and experience together in Belonging?

So, where do we go from here?
- Healing: The Thriving journey continues!

Enjoy your Party!

Belonging Exercise: Belonging party and Appreciation Story exercise
This exercise lasts for the entire class period.

Exercise Note:
- As you celebrate and share appreciation stories, share the snacks and treats you brought with others!
- Remember: You can munch while you share stories!

Instructions:

1. You do not have to remain at your Round Table for this exercise. As you munch and enjoy Belonging snacks, you are free to move around the room and share your stories with anyone in class.

2. Use your Appreciation Story Worksheet to guide you as you tell stories the 4+ way.

3. You can use the following questions and guidelines from your worksheet to guide you:
   a. What did I know about creating belonging before this class and what do I know now?
   b. What do I appreciate about my RCs when they are running better?
   c. What have I learned about cravings and attachment needs that has helped me grow?
   d. What have I learned about helping others keep their RCs on?
   e. What do I appreciate about my style for creating belonging?
   f. What do I appreciate about the belonging I have created and received in this class?
   g. What do I appreciate about my Belonging Round Table group and classmates?
   h. Appreciation stories from my Godsight moments.
   i. Good things that came out of our Star Card project.

4. Enjoy your snacks and have fun telling your stories!

5. Remember: You Belong!

CELEBRATE, SHARE STORIES AND ENJOY YOUR PARTY. YOU DESERVE IT!

Notes

Chapter 12: Questions for Further Discussion

1. From the time that Belonging class started until now, how much do you think your RCs have improved? What are the strategies that best help you return to shalom and appreciation with your RCs active?

2. Make a list of the 10 things that were most important to you throughout the Belonging class.

3. What have you learned about your own personal style of creating belonging? How do you most like to express belonging to others? Please list at least 5 ways you enjoy creating belonging.

4. Have you noticed a change in the intensity of your cravings? What strategies have been most effective for you?

5. Make a list of the top 5 signs that:
   a. You are feeling overwhelmed.
   b. Others are starting to feel overwhelmed.
   c. You are amplifying distress.
   d. You are quieting.
   e. You are dismissing and shutting down in relationship.
   f. Others have stopped listening.

6. Are there issues you have identified that you would like to work on in the Healing module? List these and be specific.

Notes

Notes

Appendix:

SHALOM FOR MY BODY: LONG VERSION

Instructions:

Like the short version of the Shalom for my Body short exercise that we learned in Belonging class, this longer version is also designed to activate our body's stress reduction systems to help calm and quiet our fear, anxiety and anger responses.

As you know, the short version of Shalom for my Body can be completed in about 1-2 minutes while remaining seated. To complete this version of the Shalom for my Body Exercise, you will need approximately 15-20 minutes. You will also need more space to lie on the floor and move around a bit. For this reason, it is helpful to have a mat, towel or blanket to lie on, or to place under your head while lying on the floor.

If you are going to try this exercise in a group, it is helpful to follow these guidelines. First, because these Shalom for my Body movements involve lying on the ground and changing positions, women will feel much more comfortable doing this exercise wearing pants - and not a dress. Second, if both men and women are doing this exercise in a group, it is a good idea to ask men to do the exercise together in the front of the room while the women move to the back of the room.

Remember: we all have different experiences with our RCs, so be sure to use what you need. If your RCs are rarely off, and if you have good results with the Shalom for my Body short form, continue to use that - and our other Belonging steps - to restore your RCs. If you have never really had your RCs on, or if the Shalom for my Body short form and other Belonging RC Restoration steps are not as effective as you would like, you may find this Shalom for my Body exercise to be more helpful.

Just like the shorter version of Shalom for my Body, this exercise is divided into 3 parts. And, like the shorter version, each part is set to scripture. The 3 parts are:

1. Part One: The Fear Bomb.

2. Part Two: The First Aid Yawn.

3. Part Three: Deep Breathing Relaxation.

The instructions for each part of this exercise start on the next page.

THE SHALOM FOR MY BODY LONG VERSION:
Like the shorter version of this exercise, the Shalom for my Body Long Version helps activate our stress reduction systems to help reduce our body's fear, anxiety and anger responses. You may find this exercise helpful if the Shalom for my Body Short Version and the other Belonging quieting and RC restoration steps have not been as effective as you would like.

Notes

Part 1: Fear Bomb

Based on Psalm 56:3 Whenever I am afraid I will trust in thee oh Lord.

This exercise starts with two basic fear responses present at birth[1] and helps you calm both reactions. In the first fear response, the body is extended and rigidly tight, and we calm by gathering in. The second fear response is curling into a tight ball, and we calm by opening up. The entire Fear Bomb Exercise is done slowly to the poetry of a Psalm.

Fear Bomb Part One

1. I lie on my back and make a stiff "X" with my body by extending my arms and legs.
2. I extend my head back so that my chin is up, and then I breathe in.
3. While bringing my legs together, head down, softly laying my hands on my chest with my elbows at my side breathe out and say, "Whenever I am afraid I will trust in thee oh Lord."
4. I smoothly repeat this exactly six times.

Fear Bomb Part Two

1. Still on my back, I bring my knees to my chest and wrap my arms tightly around my legs.
2. I recite, "Whenever I am afraid"
3. I smoothly make an "X" again but this time resting quietly and calmly.
4. I recite "I will trust in thee oh Lord."
5. I smoothly repeat this exactly seven times. (not six as the first)

Part 2: First Aid Yawn

2 Timothy 1:7 For God has not given us a spirit of fear but of power, and of love and of a sound mind. (NKJV).

Now that the Fear Bomb exercise lowered our fear, it is time to start neutralizing the stress response using a position[2] used in first aid and yawning. Yawning is a powerful trigger for your parasympathetic nervous system. The exercise is done slowly reciting a verse like poetry.

1. I lie on my stomach with my right arm at my side and my right leg straight. My head is turned to the left. My left leg is comfortably bent and my left foot is against my right knee. My left arm is bent as though I were waving and my left hand is resting against the floor.
2. I open my mouth wide and yawn slowly. (Hint: sometimes it helps to move my jaw up and down slightly after my mouth is wide open and I will get a real yawn instead of an artificial one. Either kind of yawn is fine but the real is better.)
3. I slowly recite the verse like a poem. "For God has not given us a spirit of fear but of power, and of love and of a sound mind."
4. I smoothly straighten my leg and move my arm to my side so that they are straight and resting by the time I finish saying the poem.
5. I turn my head to the right. Bend my right leg so my right foot is against my left knee. I put my right hand up like I am going to wave with the palm of my hand resting on the floor.
6. I open my mouth and yawn slowly.
7. I slowly recite the verse like a poem.

---

1. Thanks to neuropsychologist Suzanne Day, Quebec Canada www.wisechoiceeducationalservices.com.

2 Thanks to neuropsychologist Suzanne Day, Quebec Canada www.wisechoiceeducationalservices.com.

8. I smoothly straighten my leg and move my arm to my side so that they are straight and resting by the time I finish saying the poem.

9. I repeat this entire exercise four times or more.

Part 3: Deep Breathing Relaxation

Proverbs 3: 5-6 Trust in the Lord with all your heart and lean not on your own understanding. In all your ways notice him there and he will direct your paths. (Interpretation of Wilder/Khouri).

After the Fear Bomb and the First Aid Yawn have begun to help your body, this exercise helps the quieting to spread around your body and start to quiet your mind as well. You can find a more extensive set of instructions in the Restarting Workbook and Facilitators Guide, pages 24-25. Do not tighten any part of your body that is injured, weak or in pain without a doctor's permission to do this activity. If you have any spine, bone, muscle injury or doubt about your health, please skip step three.

1. I either sit or lie comfortably so I do not have to support my weight with my muscles.

2. I place my hand on my stomach and breathe deeply so that I feel my stomach expand with each breath.

3. I will skip this step if I have any medical restrictions or injuries to my body. If I am in good health, I take a deep breath and hold it while I tighten all the muscles in my body at once - but not too hard. I tighten my feet, legs, buttocks, back, stomach, chest, arms, neck and face until I am ready to exhale, then I relax and breathe out. I do this step only once.

4. I breathe out, take a deep breath and then slowly say, "I will trust in the Lord with all my heart and lean not on my own understanding" as I breathe out again.

5. I take a slow breath and then slowly say, "In all my ways I notice him there and he will direct my paths" as I breathe out.

6. I repeat steps four and five about six times.

Thriving: Recover Your Life

HOW DO THE 5 THRIVING MODULES WORK TOGETHER?

Restarting:

Restarting is the entry module for the Thriving: Recover Your Life program. Over a 12 week period in Restarting groups, you learn how you are created for joy, learn how to recognize where your brain lacks joy and how to connect with others in order to retrain your brain FOR JOY! Restarting groups combine joy building exercises, DVD teachings from Ed Khouri and the Restarting workbook, which is full of notes, follow-up questions and 12 Step applications for training. Restarting is all about retraining the brain for change - and not just understanding why we are the way we are!

Forming:

Thriving is for the whole church. Forming is also an entrance to the Thriving: Recover Your Life Program for people who want to grow their spiritual maturity by engaging at deeper levels with God. This 12 week module is all about forming your relationship with Jesus. In Forming, you will learn more about hearing God and finding your true identity in Christ. You will begin to see yourself through the eyes of heaven and recognize grace as an active force for transformation and change.

Belonging:

Your second 90 days in the Thriving Program take you through the Belonging module. You will work in small groups to restore your ability to create a joyful place for others to belong with you. Belonging jump-starts your process of learning the 19 skills that build healthy relationships and strong emotional resilience. In Belonging, you learn to recognize when your brain's relational circuits are off, quiet your distress, and return to shalom and appreciation with your relational circuits active! Creating belonging means learning not to overwhelm others, recognizing the effects of attachment pain, and learning a surprising way to control your cravings.

Healing:

Healing is the module where you can discover how to experience Jesus in the painful places of life. Jesus is the healer, and by the time participants get to this module, they have built up enough joy capacity to let Jesus do His work. We work on inner healing in the safety of groups of 3 to 5 people, and begin each exercise with God in a joyful situation! In Healing, we will learn to distinguish God's voice from our own. This module will utilize the Immanuel Process developed in connection with Dr. Karl Lehman.

Loving:

Loving is the last module in Thriving: Recover Your Life. In this module, you will take what you have learned in all the previous modules and apply it to your own relationships. You will take the joy and healing that you have been developing back to the relationships that God has placed in your life. You will practice receiving and giving good things to the people you live with and love - or wish you could.

For more information, please visit us at www.ThrivingRecovery.org.